"Thank you for your fine contribution to I
—Office o
The Whit... ....

MW00636971

"Thank you for your good book; it was well written and sorely needed."
—John D. Lange
Department of the Treasury

"The [3-Step System] has helped hundreds of thousands of travelers avoid jet lag over the last 20 years."
—U. S. Department of Energy
Argonne National Laboratory

"For the vacationer who doesn't want to miss a minute of sightseeing abroad, for the business executive who must be sharp at a meeting . . . "
—Jane Brody
New York Times

"Even with a little bending, the regimen worked well."
—Dennis R. Getto
Journalist, *Milwaukee Journal Sentinel*

"I tried it myself, and . . . [*The Cure for Jet Lag*] worked for one of the most jet-lag-prone travelers in Christendom."
—William Hines
Journalist, *Chicago Sun-Times*

"Ehret . . . has testimony from thousands of military and industrial executives who have used it [*The Cure for Jet Lag*] in the past few years."
—*Washington Post*

"Dr. Charles F. Ehret has found a way to . . . reduce or eliminate jet lag."
—*Family Weekly*

"Arm yourself with [*The Cure for Jet Lag*]."
—United Press International

" . . . a plan that's designed to ease the body into acting the way it should after a long trip by air."
—*New York Daily News*

"On the basis of a flight from Tokyo to New York, during which I followed the [3-Step System] rigorously, I experienced no disorientation. Previously, I had needed a week to recover."
—Dorothy Guyot, Ph.D.

"I have traveled the world and followed Dr. Ehret's system for twenty-five years. I will use it again in February 2008 on a trip to Buenos Aires. It makes a big difference, particularly on the first day."
—Louis J. Cohn
Chicago Attorney

" . . . your [cure] worked well for me and I arrived in Milan ready to go to work."
—Eugene Callen
CEO, Callen Manufacturing

"It worked wonderfully! The Detroit-London through-the-night-direct-to-all-day-meetings was never so easy."
—Maurita Peterson Holland
Head, Technology Libraries

" . . . it worked perfectly. I was able to do a full day's work immediately on arrival in both directions."
—F. Lincoln Vogel
University of Pennsylvania

" . . . I have used your [3-Step System] on two occasions in the last couple of months, both times with great success . . . I have in turn shared it with no less than thirty people."
—J. D. Weathers
Engineer

"My wife and I . . . were amazed at the excellent results."
—Harry Wassail
Consulting Geologist

"Going on the [3-Step System] is an essential part of preparing for any trip."
—Arlene Friedman
Mach II Travel Agency

THE
CURE
FOR
JET
LAG

2022

Victoria — Most important p. 49 thru p. 60
p. 76, 78, 79 Most
important for you.
Be sure you save this book.
Aunt Madonna

By Lynne Waller Scanlon & Charles F. Ehret, Ph.D.

Back2Press

ACKNOWLEDGMENTS
Charles F. Ehret, Ph.D.

This book reflects the industry and experiences of many people over the course of nearly sixty years of work in the field that we now know as Chronobiology. I am especially grateful to Dr. E. L. Powers of the University of Texas, who first suggested to me, in 1946, that cells may have clocks; to Drs. Van R. Potter, the University of Wisconsin, and Kenneth R. Dobra, the University of Louisville, who collaborated with me in the earliest experiments on the chronobiotic action of the methyl xanthine drugs; to Drs. John J. Wille, the Mayo Clinic, Gregory Antipa, San Francisco State University, and Kenneth R. Groh, Argonne National Laboratory, who worked in my lab at Argonne, showing that food plays a role as a circadian clock synchronizer in free living cells and later in whole animals; and to Drs. Richard Wurtman and John Fernstrom of the Massachusetts Institute of Technology, whose studies on the role of nutrition in determining neurochemical changes in the brain provoked much of the work in many parts of the world that followed up on these early studies.

There are scores of unsung pioneers who, since the earliest days of transmeridional travel, monitored resolutely their physiological and performance rhythms on many long distance trips. In the forefront of these pioneers are Drs. Franz and Erna Halberg and Dr. Erhard Haus of the University of Minnesota, Dr. L. E. Scheving of the University of Arkansas, and the late Dr. Howard Levine of the New Britain (Connecticut) General Hospital. For their contributions to our best understandings of psychomotor and psychological performance rhythms, we are indebted to Drs. Peter Colquhoun, Simon Folkard, and Timothy Monk, the University of Sussex. For their experimental studies of larger groups of human subjects in transmeridional flight, I owe a lasting debt to Drs. K. E. Klein and H. M. Wegmann of the West German Institute for Aviation Medicine, to Dr. Takashi Sasaki of Kumamoto University, and especially to Major R. Curtis Graeber of the Walter Reed Army Institute of Research.

To the many volunteers and contributors to our own system, and enthusiasts in reporting on its efficacy, I extend my thanks, especially to Henry Cernota and members of the Automotive Transportation Supervisors of Chicago, to

Acknowledgments

Joseph T. Benich and his nomadic Nomads of Detroit, to Robert Phelps of the Boston Globe, to Dr. and Mrs. James Sim of St. Catherines, Ontario, to Warren S. Tenney of New York City, and to Betty and John Menke of Scarsdale, New York. These people were in the vanguard of an increasingly appreciative and demanding public who made clear to me the need for *Overcoming Jet Lag*.

This book would never have come to fruition without the professional skill and perseverance of my talented coauthor, Lynne Waller Scanlon of New York City. It was she who guided the project through proposal development, placement of the book, and most important, translation of the esoteric terms and jargon of contemporary biological science into readable and comprehensible form for the general reader.

Special thanks go to my wife, Dorothy Armstrong Ehret, for her indefatigable secretarial help, excellent editorial assistance, and continuous encouragement through all phases of this important project.

INTRODUCTION
Lynne Waller Scanlon

Back by Popular Demand

This famous 3-Step System to cure jet lag was developed by the world's preeminent chronobiologist, Dr. Charles F. Ehret, when he was a senior scientist at Argonne National Laboratory, a research facility of the U.S. Department of Energy operated by the University of Chicago in Argonne, Illinois. Almost exactly twenty-five years ago, Dr. Ehret and I collaborated on *Overcoming Jet Lag*, a book that made the 3-Step System to cure jet lag readily available to any and all travelers. *Overcoming Jet Lag* became a bestseller, taking off and selling hundreds of thousands of copies worldwide. *The Cure for Jet Lag* is the updated version of *Overcoming Jet Lag*.

When Dr. Ehret and I discussed a revised edition of our book, he agreed readily that there was a need to "reaffirm on a broad international scale how valid the basic methods are . . ." In one of his last conversations with me, Dr. Ehret said to me that it was evident that millions of people around the world were still unaware that a cure for jet lag existed. Although the outdated and out-of-print version of our old book could be found on the Internet (often at "rare book" prices), a new edition was long overdue. *The Cure for Jet Lag,* back, if you will, by popular demand, will provide the jet-setting traveler with Dr. Ehret's simple, safe, easy-to-follow and convenient system once again.

What's new in *The Cure for Jet Lag* if the 3-Step System existed twenty-five years ago?

- A more detailed explanation of the plan.
- A treatment for caffeine withdrawal when the 3-Step System calls for the avoidance of caffeinated foods, drugs, and beverages.
- Updated examples.
- Requirements by Homeland Security, so that you don't get held up at the gate if you are carrying prepacked foods.
- An Appendix with a long (often surprising) list of caffeinated drinks and drugs.
- Expanded FAQs.

Also, the layout and design have changed. Specifically, the pages of *The Cure for Jet Lag* are much bigger and the print is larger than found in the original version in order to make *The Cure for Jet Lag* easier to read in the dim light of an airplane cabin as you wing your way through time zone after time zone.

A Word About the Late Dr. Charles F. Ehret

My coauthor, Dr. Ehret, died at 83 in February of 2007. News of his death resulted in an outpouring of sympathy from friends and colleagues around the world and a Resolution by the Senate of the Ninety-Fifth General Assembly of the State of Illinois in which the Assembly officially joined his family and friends in mourning his passing.

Not only was Dr. Ehret the world's most famous chronobiologist, I could not have asked for a better coauthor. He was an amazing man.

He also was the husband of Dorothy and the father of eight. He served in the U. S. Army's 87th Infantry Division during World War II, receiving a Bronze Star and a Purple Heart for actions during the Battle of the Bulge.

TABLE OF CONTENTS

ACKNOWLEDGMENTS   v
by Charles F. Ehret, Ph.D.

INTRODUCTION   vii
by Lynne Waller Scanlon

ONE   **JET LAG—THE TRAVELER'S #1 COMPLAINT**   1
Blame it on Orville and Wilbur! • A Cure for Jet Lag from Argonne
National Laboratory • The Phenomenon of Too Rapid East/West
Flight • The Chronobiological and Biochemical Basis of Jet Lag
The Double Whammy of Jet Lag and Homesickness

TWO   **THE ESCALATING SYMPTOMS OF JET LAG**   13
Garden Variety Fatigue • Early Symptoms • Later
Symptoms • Duration of Symptoms: With and Without
The Cure for Jet Lag • Time Zone Factors • Personality
Factors • Social Factors • Age Factors • Health Factors

THREE   **WHAT YOU NEED TO KNOW ABOUT TIME ZONES**   25
Time Structure and the Planet Earth • Mercator Map—Time
Zones of the World • Differences Between Standard U.S. Time
Zones and Foreign Countries • Ribbons of Cities—Location of
Landmark Cities According to World Time Zones

FOUR   **TRICKING BODY CLOCKS TO A NEW TIME ZONE**   41
Old Remedies versus *The Cure for Jet Lag* • Origins of *The Cure
for Jet Lag* 3-Step System • Major Influences on Body Clocks

Table of Contents

FIVE   **HOW *THE CURE FOR JET LAG* WORKS**   **49**

The 3-Step System • Overcoming Jet Lag with Light and Dark
Overcoming Jet Lag with Specific Foods • Overcoming Jet Lag
with Carefully Timed Coffee or Tea • Overcoming Jet Lag with
High and Low Calorie Meals • Overcoming Jet Lag with
Physical and Mental Activity

SIX   **HOW TO CHOOSE THE RIGHT 3-STEP SYSTEM**   **61**

Eastbound, Westbound and Complex Flight Plans • Timing
Departure and Arrival Times • Eastbound Flights • Westbound
Flights • Four Questions to Ask Your Airline • Preflight, Inflight
and Postflight Tip Sheet

SEVEN   **EASTBOUND FLIGHTS**   **68**

Eastbound 1-2 Time Zones • Eastbound 3-4 Time Zones
Eastbound 5-6 Time Zones • Eastbound 7-8 Time Zones
Eastbound 9-10 Time Zones • Eastbound 11-12 Time Zones

EIGHT   **WESTBOUND FLIGHTS**   **92**

Westbound 1-2 Time Zones • Westbound 3-4 Time Zones
Westbound 5-6 Time Zones • Westbound 7-8 Time Zones
Westbound 9-10 Time Zones • Westbound 11-12 Time Zones

NINE   **COMPLEX FLIGHTS**   **113**

Multi-Destination Flights and Multiple Time Zone Changes
Multi-Destination Flights, Same Direction—Short Stay
Multi-Destination Flights, Same Direction—Relatively
Brief Length of Stay • Multi-Destination Flights, East/West
and West/East—Short Stay • Multi-Destination Flights,
East/West and West/East—Varying Length of Stay
Multi-Destination Flights, Any Direction—Long Length
of Stay • Itinerary Worksheet

TEN   **FREQUENTLY ASKED QUESTIONS**   **119**

You Bet You Have Questions!

ELEVEN   **MENTAL AND PHYSICAL EXERCISE PROGRAM**   **125**

Rise and Shine on Destination Time! • Waking Your Body Up in Time for a New Time Zone • Waking Your Mind Up in Time for a New Time Zone

TWELVE   **3-STEP SYSTEM PREFLIGHT, INFLIGHT**   **127**
           AND POSTFLIGHT MEALS & MENUS

Feasting and Fasting (Eating Lightly) • Suggested Menus Selecting the Right Foods for Postflight Meals • Composition of Foods/Calorie Counter

THIRTEEN   **SPECIAL PEOPLE/SPECIAL INFORMATION**   **143**

Shift Workers (Doctors, Nurses, Police, Fire Personnel Factory Workers) • Gamblers • Athletes • Anyone Taking Drugs • Women • The Elderly • Pilots and Air Crew Members Midnight Fliers • Travelers By Sea

APPENDIX   **LIST OF BEVERAGES AND FOODS**   **151**

List of Caffeinated Beverages and Foods • Itinerary Worksheet

                ABOUT THE AUTHORS   **165**

CHAPTER ONE
JET LAG—THE TRAVELER'S #1 COMPLAINT

Blame it on Orville and Wilbur!

It was those Wright brothers! Had not Orville and Wilbur taken to the skies and invented the aircraft controls that made mechanical fixed wing flight possible in the early 1900s, "jet lag" might never have entered our lexicon, let alone quickly become the scourge of rapid travel in the 20th Century. It was the Wright brothers' invention that enabled the industrialist and aviator Howard Hughes and TWA president Jack Frye to fly eastward in 1944 from Burbank, California to Washington, D.C. in just 6 hours and 57 minutes, ushering in the era of rapid time zone change and . . . jet lag.

Of course, no one knew anything about jet lag or jet lag symptoms prior to Howard Hughes' flight to Washington because no one had ever traveled so far so fast before 1944. But as rapid time-zone-crossing travel increased and more and more people packed their bags and flew to places where they had to adjust their wristwatches ahead or back to a new time zone, it became very clear very quickly that shortly after landing, something terribly debilitating was taking place, physically and mentally. Tremendous fatigue and mental confusion washed over the traveler within twenty-four hours. What was occurring would eventually be officially labeled by scientists as *circadian dyschronism* . . . and commonly referred to as the much-dreaded jet lag by international executives, diplomats and tourists.

Yet, despite the multitude of sufferers *and the availability of a cure*, only a handful of scientists specializing in chronobiology (the study of how time affects living organisms) and circadian regulatory biology (the study of how to control daily body rhythms[1]) can tell you about the real cause, the true nature of jet lag's body-wide effect . . . and that a simple, safe, convenient cure for jet lag exists.

---

[1] Not to be confused with "biorhythms," which have no scientific basis.

A Cure for Jet Lag from Argonne National Laboratory

The irony in this situation is that over the twenty-five years since the original book, the international best-seller *Overcoming Jet Lag*, was published, jet lag should have become an ailment relegated to the past. All the steps necessary—preflight, inflight and postflight—that could take the serious "lag" out of jet travel were made available to the public through the book and from Argonne National Laboratory. (Over the years Argonne National Laboratory received more than 500,000 requests for more information.) And even though the U. S. Army's Rapid Deployment Force, hundreds of thousands of professional athletes, business people, and diplomats routinely use the 3-Step System for their multi-time-zone flights, for the most part, knowledge about the cure for jet lag has not reached millions of travelers flying cross-continent and around the globe each year.

So jet lag continues to ruin more vacations, botch more business meetings, and wreak more general havoc on the air traveler than all other preflight and inflight irritations combined. That's why "jet lag" remains a household word to the millions of passengers who have flown coast to coast in the United States, millions who have flown abroad from the United States (actually, 8 million or so, annually, according to the U. S. Office of Travel & Tourism), and millions from around the globe who have passed through the world's international airports.

The Phenomenon of Too Rapid East/West Flight

Once and for all, let's clear up the misconception that jet lag is caused by being enclosed in a vehicle that is traveling at great speeds at terrifically high altitudes. Air travelers erroneously tend to correlate speed and altitude with jet lag. In fact, the inflight velocity of the airplane and the distance traveled above the earth, per se, have absolutely nothing do with jet lag. Nor do the common inflight symptoms of ear-popping, light headedness, dehydration, irritability, motion sickness, and other ailments about which air travelers often complain while en route. Instead, all these problems can be attributed to immobility, poor cabin pressure, drinking alcoholic beverages while in flight, and nerve-wracking engine noises—but not jet lag. Jet lag is strictly a phenomenon of long distance, too rapid travel east/west or west/east from one time frame to another.

Man lacks innate travel instincts. As the Wright brothers took to the air, geographic restrictions automatically placed on man as an earthbound animal were lifted, bestowing him with the ability to "fly with the eagles"—but without any corresponding travel instincts to slow down, lay over, or take a few days or weeks to ease into a new time zone. He never developed the bird's inner voice or the whale's instinct to keep him traveling in the "proper" direction.

During the course of evolution, those animals that developed the ability to fly or swim great distances through time zones simultaneously developed an ingrained set of instructions to protect them from the symptoms associated with rapid east/west travel. For example, the Canada goose, which flies thousands of miles each year during migration, responds to an instinct that limits the easterly or westerly range of flight. Those few species of birds that do fly great distances in an easterly or westerly direction invariably proceed in stages, stopping and resting for several days in each location before resuming their journey. The gray whale swims the entire length of the West Coast from Alaska to Mexico; yet if you chart his course, you will see that he, too, travels much more north to south than west to east.

Limitations upon man's movements were imposed upon him by the pace he could set with his own feet, the speed and stamina of the animals that he domesticated and rode, the strength of his stroke when he paddled a canoe, or his ability to build a seaworthy vessel and be transported by the winds. For man to travel great distances over the earth required weeks, months, years, or even generations.

Nowadays, man soars encapsulated in a jet plane from east to west or west to east with an abandon beyond the widest extremes of any winged or finned creature on earth.

Yet, still possessed of essentially a Stone Age body that should be traveling great distances very, very slowly, if at all, man suffers the consequences in the form of jet lag.

The Chronobiological and Biochemical Basis of Jet Lag

The universe is filled with cycles within cycles within cycles. As we all know, each planet orbits the sun in an individual planetary year, 365 days for the planet earth. Within the earth's planetary year there is a cycle of four seasons: spring, summer, fall, and winter. The moon waxes and wanes in the light of the sun about every twenty-seven days as it revolves around the earth.

The Chronobiological and Biochemical Basis of Jet Lag

In tune with the cyclic universe, we humans resonate in time with our own cycles, many of which have been studied and charted by chronobiologists. These studies reveal that our bodies are controlled by a master clock in the brain and interrelated satellite "time-keepers" situated throughout the body. Precision-timed, the satellites adjust and readjust, turning on, speeding up, slowing down and turning off all our biochemical processes throughout the day in an elaborate minuet. In definite cyclical patterns, the time-keepers control our hormone levels, blood pressure, body temperature, digestive enzymes, kidneys, bladder, heart and brainwaves, and see that all our internal systems are synchronized not only with one another, but with the external cycles of our world as well.

The master clock and satellite time-keepers take their cues from several major sources in our immediate environment. The level of artificial illumination, brightness of sunlight, and clock-time-of-day (external cues); food, drugs, and medication (internal cues); work, exercise, and periods of personal interaction (social cues) combine to lock in and reinforce our sense of time as they synchronize what is known to the scientific community as circadian rhythms,[2] and to the rest of us as daily body rhythms.

The synchronization of these crucial rhythms relies heavily on the presence of consistent daily patterns. Different time frames and unexpected cues disrupt our body rhythms. When we quickly transport ourselves halfway around the globe, the unfamiliar timing of the external, internal, and social cues around us initiate a biochemical phase shift that stimulates the onset of jet lag. This shift triggers a major disruption in the synchronization of the timekeepers and body rhythms that keep our heart pumping to one beat while our lungs inhale and exhale to another, that put us to sleep at night and wake us in the morning, and that control the timing of every function of our body—right down to the level of a single cell.

When we board a jet plane and fly with or against the rotation of the earth, upon landing we have to reset not only our wristwatch to reflect local time, but our entire twenty-four-hour internal biochemical timetable as well. That required shift is at the root of jet lag.

---

[2] As in "*circa* 1776, Paul Revere made silver," *circa* means "about"; *dian* comes from the Latin word *dies*, for "one day." *Circadian* therefore equals "about one day." In the late 1940s, Franz Halberg, M.D., a professor at the University of Minnesota, coined the word "circadian" after he noticed rhythmic variations throughout the day in the count of white blood cells in laboratory animals.

Scientists describe the traveler after an easterly or westerly flight as being in a *transient state of dyschronism*. In a sense the "hands" of the billions of body clocks that exist within our body begin to spin as they search for a new schedule that will enable our systems to resynchronize. Until this resynchronization runs its course, our well-defined "old" body rhythms play tug-of-war with the still-to-be-defined "new" body rhythms that must develop as our body internalizes a different sense of time and place.

Of course, since jet lag occurs when we change time frames, it is strictly a phenomenon of time zones crossed during east/west flight, not north/south flight. We can fly thousands of miles from Boston to Lima, Peru, and not experience jet lag; thousands miles from Chicago to Mexico City and feel fine; and thousands of miles from Nome, Alaska, to Papeete, Tahiti—only an hour's difference—and adjust very quickly. When we travel in an essentially northerly or southerly direction we do not change more than one or two time zones.

However, if we fly east/west from Bangor to Los Angeles and experience more than a three hour time difference, we can expect moderate jet lag. Or, if we fly north/south from Chicago and combine it with an east/west angle that brings us to New Zealand— a six-hour difference—we can count on starting to experience major jet lag.

Note that jet lag starts when we have to adjust not only our wristwatch to reflect a different local time, but also our own daily internal biological rhythms of sleeping and waking, digestion and elimination, on the basis of a new time and new place. That is why jet lag commonly begins when we step out of the airplane, and not while we are still en route.

Compounding the problem is the fact that body rhythms exhibit a kind of lingering memory that resists change. In order to keep us running smoothly, they cling to the same old familiar schedule based on past time cues. The old rhythms corresponding to when the sun would have risen or set back home—when our alarm would have gone off, when we would have eaten, when we would have used the toilet and when we would have been working or socializing—each of these old rhythms persists tenaciously. Our internal clocks, still expecting breakfast on our hometown schedules, prepare for it by releasing enzymes and stomach acids in anticipation of receiving food—yet in all likelihood we will not eat any food, because it was mid-afternoon in Rome when we landed and dinner is still a couple of hours away.

Similarly, even though the sun may just be rising in India when we disembark from the airplane, our internal clock is programmed to promote sleep on hometown time and consequently our mental processes are shutting down just when we probably need them the most. Conversely, after landing in Japan in total darkness, we might find that we cannot sleep because our bodies still believe that it's really morning and therefore our minds remain fully alert. This transient state means only one thing: until our bodies can adapt to the new time frame, be it hours ahead or hours behind, we'll have jet lag.

The following is a list of human cycles—rapid, daily, weekly/monthly, yearly—that are disrupted by jet lag.

Cycles Disturbed by Jet Lag			
Rapid (Ultradian)	Daily (Circadian)	Weekly/Monthly (Infradian)	Yearly (Circannual)

Heart
  Heart beat
  Pulse rate
Lungs
  Breathing
Cell division
Eye blinking
Swallowing
Brain waves
	Heart
	  Blood pressure
	  Blood clotting
	Eyesight
	  Visual acuity
	Mental ability
	  Alertness
	  Cognitive
	    function
	Physical ability
	  Strength
	  Energy levels
	  Sense of pain
	Sleep/wake
	Digestion
	  Bowel
	    movements
	  Urinary output
	  Hunger pangs
	Reproduction
	  Hormone levels
	Temperature
	Metabolism
	Sense of time
	Hair growth
	  Beard
		Reproduction
		  Ovulation
		  Menstruation
		  Hormone levels
			Life span
			  Infancy
			  Puberty
			  Adulthood
			  Old age
			Reproduction
			  Conception
			  Birth
			  Hormone levels
			Cell replacement

Ultimately, the external, internal, and social cues at our flight destination will persuade the body clocks to reset themselves. The rise and set of the sun will exert an irresistible pressure on our body rhythms of sleep and wakefulness to "get in sync" with the new time frame, as it will when we eat our meals and when we socialize. In the interim without the 3-Step System we will experience a transient state of mental and physical "cellular" chaos—jet lag—as our body rhythms reluctantly begin to break their old daily patterns and shift to the new schedule in a new time frame.

The Double Whammy of Jet Lag and Homesickness

We know that every creature on earth is equipped with a wide variety of innate detection and measuring systems that are traditionally referred to as senses. In man, five senses exist that allow us to see, hear, feel, taste, and smell. Yet to scientists specializing in chronobiology and regulatory biology, three other more abstract, but equally important, senses exist: sense of place, sense of time and, as a byproduct of both, sense of well-being.

Sense of Place. All locations are physically, geographically, and even chemically different from one another, whether dramatically or subtly. All living organisms have a keen sense of place and express it either consciously or unconsciously. Human beings consciously become "homesick" for familiar surroundings and wish for their own beds, while unconsciously they yearn for the accustomed hometown patterns of something as simple as the time frame of the sunrise and sunset. In other animals, like the salmon, their sense of place is so acute that it enables them to turn virtually mid-stream or mid-ocean and unerringly return to their place of origin.

Sense of Time. All plants and animals possess a natural, ingrained sense of time and timing tied to their sense of place. In plants, their sense of time causes the blossoms of the chrysanthemum to burst open one day and the flowers of the poinsettia yet another day. In animals, including man, every cell produces proteins and gene products in accordance with a preordained system that takes about a day to run, and responds to the distinctive qualities of six in the morning, noon, and midnight. In animals other than man, as if a switch were thrown, sense of time makes them change their course, migrate, store food, or hibernate.

A Short History of Homesickness

The symptoms of homesickness were mentioned long ago in the Old Testament *Book of Exodus* and in Homer's *Odyssey*, although the actual term "homesickness" didn't enter the lexicon until 1688 when Johannes Hofer (1669-1752) coined the phrase *mal du pays* or "homesickness" to describe "a sad mood originating from the desire for return to one's native land." At the time, homesickness was a disease of epidemic proportions among Swiss mercenaries deployed to the lowlands of France and Italy by European Kings. Because soldiers sat around a camp fire at night singing nostalgic songs about the old country, it was thought that singing itself was the cause of homesickness. However, when soldiers were forbidden to sing about their native homelands, they still longed for home to the point of desertion, illness or death.

A number of harebrained remedies were tried to alleviate homesickness, including bloodletting, purging, opium, leeches, "warm hypnotic emulsions," and a "pressure differential" treatment in which soldiers were "confined to high towers, given doses of compressed air and rotated rapidly in swivel chairs." In 1733, a Russian army officer allegedly found a sure-cure for homesickness among his troops. He buried a homesick soldier alive, and the incidence of homesickness or nostalgia dramatically decreased.

Of course, while returning to home and hearth may be the sure cure for homesickness, it isn't always possible to be discharged and sent home. Troops often have to "soldier on." Today, all armies regard "the mail" as a priority for fighting troops second only to ammunition, and the United States does its best to replicate features of a typical America town wherever troops are deployed abroad.

Lambert, Craig. "Hypochondria of the Heart." Harvard Magazine. September - October 2001 http://harvardmagazine.com/2001/09/hypochondria-of-the-hear.html

Wikipedia Contributors. "Homesickness." Wikipedia, The Free Encyclopedia. Date of Last Revision: 12 July 2008. http://en.wikipedia.org/wiki/Homesickness

Sense of Well-Being. Inextricably dependent on sense of place and sense of time is sense of well-being. Rapidly crossing time zones disrupts both sense of time and sense of place, and therefore also sense of well-being. The disruption of sense of time triggers jet lag. The additional disruption of sense of place as you pick up physically and move to strange surroundings, triggers a disruption in sense of well-being. That disruption can bring on what is commonly known as "homesickness."

Homesickness, while not chronobiological dyschronism or jet lag, is a very serious problem associated with travel. If you've ever experienced homesickness, you know how very painful it can be. You feel disoriented, fatigued, depressed and heavy-hearted. You lose your appetite. You can't sleep. You think constantly of home and long to return to familiar surroundings.

Diplomats assigned to foreign countries, travelers spending weeks or months abroad, teenagers matriculating at colleges thousands of miles from home, all are susceptible to a tidal wave of homesickness that can descend like a dark cloud within a few days after arriving in a new town or country.

The longing for familiar surroundings, friends and family, brought on by a disrupted sense of place, sense of time and sense of well-being, combined with the body-wide, biochemical cellular chaos caused by real jet lag, can result in a double whammy of misery. That's the bad news. The good news is that the instructions found in *The Cure for Jet Lag* postflight steps will not only counter jet lag symptoms, but have the ability to help lift the mental and physical symptoms of homesickness.

Examples of Famous People & Jet Lag

From John Foster Dulles to President George W. Bush

Decades of Famous Jet Lag Sufferers!

In 1959, in a death-bed interview, former Secretary of State John Foster Dulles admitted that he felt his decision on the controversial Aswan Dam in Egypt was one of the great mistakes of his life, and that he might have taken a more conciliatory stance with the Egyptians had he not been so weary from jet travel.

• • • •

In 1963, Lowell Thomas, the famous radio and film commentator who pioneered the very first broadcasts from an airplane and from a ship, and whose sonorous baritone reached billions during his forty-five-year career, was hospitalized because of muscular tremors, extreme fatigue, fainting and vertigo. The physicians attending Thomas thought he had had a heart attack, but the diagnosis could not be confirmed through traditional medical methods. Suddenly, the crux of the problem dawned on Thomas when he realized that he had been crisscrossing the globe for months in pursuit of news stories. He guessed he had probably crossed all twenty-four time zones at least twice. He wasn't having a heart attack. He was suffering from severe jet lag symptoms masquerading as a heart attack.

• • • •

In 1977, Hiram Pong retired from the United States Senate because the 9,116-mile airplane trip between his home in Hawaii and his office in Washington, D.C. was too debilitating. He traveled from Hawaii to work eighteen times a year and suffered from a chronic state of jet lag.

• • • •

In 1978, author Andrew M. Greeley admitted in *The Making of the Popes* that on his first day at his hotel in Rome, he felt he was "going to pieces." He had lost his glasses, walked out of the hotel without his wallet, forgotten phone numbers, and was in "mortal terror" of missing his appointments. He had jet lag.

• • • •

In 1979, Greg Louganis, a Gold Medalist on the United States Olympic Diving Team, reported on NBC's "Sports Year '79—A Salute to the Champions" that the reason he had struck his head on the ten-meter platform during a competition in the Soviet Union was because his acrobatic skills and precision timing had been dramatically affected by jet lag. He was unconscious for twenty minutes after being pulled out of the water.

In 2000, according to the University of Georgia, World and Olympic champion sprinter Maurice Greene blamed jet lag for his loss to Portugal's Francis Obikwelu in the 100 meters at the Gaz de France Track Meet. In 2002, BBC Sport reported that Greene "complained of jet lag after clocking a pedestrian time of 10.56 seconds in the Yokohama Super Track and Field Meet" while losing to fellow American Tim Montgomery. In 2004, Greene lost again to Obikwelu at the Paris Golden League meeting and stated: "Of course it's a disappointment, but I knew it was going to be hard as I only arrived here two days ago . . . My body is very tired, which you will have seen from my time."

• • • •

In 2005, according to BBC News, while President George W. Bush was in Beijing, a reporter asked him to explain why he seemed "a little off [his] game" while appearing to "rush" through a reading of his statement during his visit with President Hu. "Have you ever heard of jet lag?" the president asked. President Bush then "strode from the lectern to the door, trying both handles and then breaking into a laugh. An aide escorted him to the correct exit and on to dinner at the Great Hall of the People."

• • • •

In 2007, John Stamos, the Emmy nominated actor in the TV series ER, was thought to be drunk when he was interviewed on TV shows in Australia. He was described as "bleary-eyed, staggering and slurring," as well as "tired and emotional" by a Sydney newspaper. Stamos appeared "disheveled" and made inane comments in which he likened himself to Elvis Presley and Princess Diana. His physical and mental state was captured for posterity by YouTube.com with the headline: "John Stamos Drunk or Jet Lag—You Decide." Stamos later blamed his unkempt state and blithering comments on the effects of jet lag.

CHAPTER TWO
THE ESCALATING SYMPTOMS OF JET LAG

Garden Variety Fatigue

If your trip has been in a north/south direction and you feel tired when you leave the airplane, the problem is likely to be the garden variety of physical fatigue brought on by pressures associated with preparing for the trip—all the minutiae associated with finally being able to lock the front door and leave for the airport. In addition, having to lug suitcases, tote bags, cameras, and briefcases to the car, bus, or train, as well as being to be forced to sit in a cramped position for hours, will have taken their toll on how you feel, but that's not jet lag. In north/south travel you do not change time zones, you recuperate quickly physically and mentally, and you do not experience jet lag.

The situation is vastly different when you have undertaken an east/west flight. Although the same garden variety fatigue will be present for the exact same reasons after the flight, if you have not employed the *The Cure for Jet Lag*, simple fatigue will soon be followed by far more pervasive mental and physical debilitation.

Early Symptoms

Although each traveler's physical and mental makeup is as individual as his fingerprints and therefore not everyone has every symptom that jet lag can produce, it is not unusual for people who have taken a long east/west flight to develop similar first-day symptoms of jet lag. These symptoms are far different from those that develop as a result of simply being tired, and without the 3-Step System they will not be remedied by a day of rest and recuperation.

Initially, on the first day at your destination, you begin to notice that you have an ever-growing sense of exhaustion that is far more pronounced than the general fatigue you might have felt as you left the airplane. It is an allover, all-consuming weariness that affects not just your sense of well-being, but your concentration, memory, and performance as well.

Later Symptoms

Relentlessly, within hours of landing at your destination, the general fatigue and first-day early jet lag symptoms advance to an even more crushing level of enervation. Without *The Cure for Jet Lag* to reduce the severity of symptoms or eliminate them entirely, jet lag now produces significant gastrointestinal disorders of constipation or diarrhea, not to mention insomnia, loss of appetite, headache, impaired night vision, and limited peripheral vision. The symptoms become body-wide and often debilitating.

To an athlete flying in from California a day or two before running in the New York City Marathon®, jet lag means that he or she will be competing while physically and mentally handicapped against local athletes whose body rhythms are running smoothly, or to those who have arrived early enough to adjust naturally and get over jet lag. Similarly, a couple just returning to Iowa from a vacation in Amsterdam will be putting themselves in a situation weighted toward trouble if quick reflexes and good vision are required during the drive from the airport to home; and a woman arriving in London from Bangor, Maine who attempts to cross the street may forget that traffic flows on the "wrong" side of the road in England and inadvertently step out into the street, having looked left when she should have looked right, and then not having had the rapid response ability necessary to get out of the way of oncoming traffic.

Duration of Symptoms:
With and Without *The Cure for Jet Lag*

How long does it take for the body to readjust to a new time zone? In an effort to find out, international researchers have studied man and laboratory rats on both real and simulated jet flights around the world. By carefully monitoring body rhythms before departure, during flight, and after arrival at the destination, and then once again after the return home, these researchers were able to establish what normal body rhythms are, record how quickly and severely they are disrupted by a time change, and determine how long the symptoms of this disruption—or jet lag—lasts.

Scientists have concluded that a person's internal body clocks are synchronized to each other, but adjust to time-zone changes at their own rates. In other words, all body clocks do not shift simultaneously. In the human body, the disrupted body clocks are thrown into cellular chaos by time zone changes. Until each and every body clock has adjusted to the new time frame and become synchronized, jet lag continues.

That is why on a trip that requires a five-hour to eight-hour time change (for example, a trip from the United States to Germany) *without* jet lag countermeasures, scientists have found it can take anywhere from four days to two weeks for sleep patterns to adjust thoroughly. Heart rate, which is normally faster in the day than at night, can take from five to eight days to synchronize without the *The Cure for Jet Lag*. Urinary output, which generally decreases during the night, can take up to eight or even ten days to normalize. The gastrointestinal system, which controls the bowels, can take twenty-four hours per time zone crossed before elimination routines readjust. Reactions to light signals, grip strength, and ability to calculate mathematical problems can take from two days to nearly two weeks to straighten out. Elementary psychomotor performance, coordination and reflexes can take from five to ten days to recover.

The following chart contains a list of early-onset jet lag symptons that you can expect to experience shortly after your arrival at your destination if you don't follow *The Cure for Jet Lag* 3-Step System. As you can see in the second column of the chart, these symptons are quickly followed by a predictable onslaught of even more debilitating symptoms.

Early and Late Jet Lag Symptoms	
Early Symptoms	**Late Symptoms**
Fatigue	Constipation or diarrhea
Disorientation	Lack of sexual interest
Reduced physical ability	Limited peripheral vision
Reduced mental acuity	Decreased muscle tone
Confusion	Impaired night vision
Upset appetite	Reduced physical work capacity
Off-schedule bowel and urinary movements	Disrupted phases of body rhythms and functions
Onset of memory loss	Slowed response time to visual stimulation
	Reduced motor coordination
	Interference with prescription drugs
	Insomnia
	Acute fatigue
	Loss of appetite
	Headache

Duration of Symptoms: With and Without *The Cure for Jet Lag*

The following table indicates how dramatically and quickly *The Cure for Jet Lag* reduces symptoms of fatigue—by almost 50% on your first day at your destination after crossing seven time zones. By the second day your symptons of fatigue are barely noticeable. In comparison, the control-group travelers who did not use *The Cure for Jet Lag* are still struggling with waves of fluctuating fatigue on the fourth day.

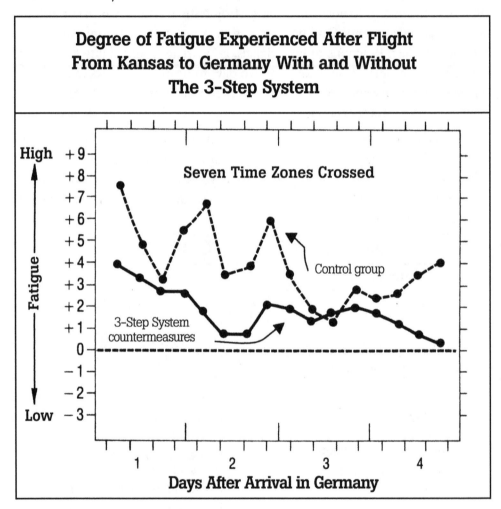

Degree of Fatigue Experienced After Flight From Kansas to Germany With and Without The 3-Step System

Seven Time Zones Crossed

Control group

3-Step System countermeasures

Fatigue — High +9 +8 +7 +6 +5 +4 +3 +2 +1 0 −1 −2 −3 Low

Days After Arrival in Germany

1   2   3   4

The following two tables indicate the amount of time required to resynchronize specific body functions **without** *The Cure for Jet Lag* to eliminate symptoms (short trips) or greatly reduce them (long trips).

Typical Resynchronization Period (in days) After Time Zone Changes (Without the Use of the 3-Step System) EASTBOUND FLIGHTS

	Time Zone Change (in hours)					
	2 hours	4 hours	6 hours	8 hours	10 hours	12 hours
Performance (psychomotor)	3	6-7	9-10	12	12	12+
Reaction time (vigilance)	1-2	3-4	5	6-7	8	8
Heart rate	2	4	6	8	8-10	8-10
Corticosteroids (urinary)	4	7-8	11-12	12	12	12+
Noradrenaline (urinary)	1	2	3	4	4-5	4-5
Adrenaline (urinary)	2	4	6	8	8-10	8-10
Bowel movements	3	6-7	9-10	12	12	12+
Body temperature	3	6	9	12	12	12+
Sleep pattern	1	3-4	4-5	6-7	8-9	8-9

Typical Resynchronization Period (in days) After Time Zone Changes (Without the Use of the 3-Step System) WESTBOUND FLIGHTS

	Time Zone Change (in hours)					
	2 hours	4 hours	6 hours	8 hours	10 hours	12 hours
Performance (psychomotor)	2	4	6	8	10	12+
Reaction time (vigilance)	1	1-2	2-3	3	4	5-8
Heart rate	1-2	2-3	4	5-6	6-7	8-10
Corticosteroids (urinary)	2-3	5	7-8	10-11	12	12+
Noradrenaline (urinary)	1	1-2	2	2-3	3-4	4-5
Adrenaline (urinary)	1-2	2-3	4	5-6	6-7	8-10
Bowel movements	2-3	4-5	7	9	11	12+
Body temperature	2	4	6	8	10	12+
Sleep pattern	1	2	3-4	4-5	6-7	8-9

How effective is the 3-Step System? Take a look at the two tables below. As you can see, the 3-Step System can have a profound effect on the severity and duration of jet lag symptoms and can, in fact, eliminate them altogether on the less extreme time zone changes.

General Comparison (in days) of Duration of Symptoms With and Without the 3-Step System
EASTBOUND FLIGHTS

Time Zone Changes	With 3-Step System*	Without 3-Step System
+2	0	3
+4	0	6
+6	1	9
+8	2	12
+10	3	12
+12	3	12+

* Any jet lag symptoms experienced while on the 3-Step System
will be greatly reduced in potential severity

General Comparison (in days) of Duration of Symptoms With and Without the 3-Step System
WESTBOUND FLIGHTS

Time Zone Changes	With 3-Step System*	Without 3-Step System
-2	0	2
-4	0	4
-6	1	6
-8	1	8
-10	2	10
-12	3	12

* Any jet lag symptoms experienced while on the 3-Step System
will be greatly reduced in potential severity

Although *The Cure for Jet Lag* can dramatically decrease the overall period of adjustment on long trips and even eliminate it on very short trips, during the course of their investigation scientists also discovered that jet lag symptoms can be affected by a myriad of seemingly disparate factors, including the number of time zones through which you pass, your own personality, eating habits and, surprisingly, the nature of social or business pressures that force you to get up and get going.

What follows is a breakdown of mitigating factors that are beyond the reach of *The Cure for Jet Lag* that can affect the duration of symptoms experienced by air travelers.

Time Zone Factors

Long Haul versus Short Haul. Obviously, the more time zones through which you pass, the more severe the body clock upheaval and jet lag symptoms. Not surprisingly, if you fly halfway around the world, your jet lag symptoms will be much more severe and last much longer than if you opt for a trip that is a quarter as long.

Also, recovery from a westbound trip is from 30% to 50% swifter than from an eastbound one. Although no one is quite certain why east-to-west flights cause less circadian rhythm disruption than flights in the opposite direction, experience shows that "losing" time is easier for the human body to handle. A handy way to remember this east to west phenomenon is contained in the words of the American writer Horace Greeley, who was renowned for his advice to the youth of his day to *"Go West, young man."*

Personality Factors

Evening versus Daytime. Many people describe themselves as "morning" types. If you leap out of bed, get dressed, and get going while "night" types are rising and falling back into bed three times prior to actually getting up, you are a morning person. When it comes to jet lag, the night owl seems to fare better when traveling in a westerly direction, whereas the morning lark does better traveling west-to-east. According to Drs. K. E. Klein and H. M. Wegmann of the former West German Institute for Aviation Medicine, this is because *"evening types seem not to experience sleep deficiency, and more easily extend the sleep period when sleep onset is shifted to late hours."*

Extrovert versus Introvert. If you are gregarious and enjoy talking, mixing with people, and doing things in a group, you are less likely to experience severe jet lag than a fellow traveler who retreats to his room upon arrival, prefers to see the sights alone, eats supper by himself, and generally leads a more reclusive existence. Exposing yourself to outside visual and mental stimuli causes chemical changes to take place in your brain to help keep you more alert, offsetting to some extent one of jet lag's effects .

Regimented versus Flexible. If you get up when the alarm goes off, eat a snack at precisely the same time every morning, head out for lunch at exactly lunchtime, have supper on the table at the same time every night, and retire without fail right after the late night news, you live by the clock and are a regimented person. If you prefer to rise at varying times, eating snacks and main meals only when hunger pangs arise, and call it a day when you actually feel like going to sleep, you are a flexible person. Of these two types, the more regimented personality will experience less jet lag. Accustomed to doing things by the clock, this type marches more readily to a new circadian beat.

Stable versus Neurotic. Anxious people secrete many hormones and neurotransmitters that unsettle body rhythms. The less easily frazzled you are by circumstance, the more easily you will adapt to a new time zone. If you are keyed-up all the time, your body rhythms will have a more difficult time adjusting to an entirely new schedule.

Social Factors

Pressured versus Relaxed. If you simply cannot give in to jet lag symptoms because you need to attend an important meeting, give a concert performance, compete in a contest or make it to another airplane, bus, or train on time, the demands of the situation may enable you to rise above jet lag, if not totally, at least temporarily. Despite the presence of jet lag, by dint of sheer will you can force yourself to function to the best of your ability and thereby accomplish much more than if you surrendered to jet lag without a fight. Once you begin to function, other factors, such as environmental and social cues, combine to help you maintain your level of activity.

Age Factors

Youth versus Middle Age versus Old Age. Although the very young may not appear to their parents to experience jet lag, they do. Infants' body rhythms are actually heavily involved in waking/sleeping cycles. An infant's waking/sleeping pattern just happens to be different from that of adults. However, infants adjust more rapidly than older people.

Body rhythm patterns are based loosely on the twelve daylight hours and twelve nighttime hours. If you are middle-aged—neither young nor old—and experience a time zone change, jet lag sets in, but it is overcome as the old light/dark pattern eventually gives way to a shifted pattern.

Possibly because of weakened or exhausted internal time-setters produced by the aging process, if you are elderly, you may suffer the most severe form of jet lag. Body rhythms of the aged tend to be already in a process of slipping out of synchronization with the twelve/twelve pattern and into predictable "circadian desynchronization," whether they have changed time zones or not.

If you are leading an increasingly more sedentary life, you may have noticed that your sleep patterns have altered significantly since middle age. Part of this is compensation for a less demanding schedule. You no longer require as much sleep, and often, when it comes, it is fragmented. (In fact, by age sixty-five, 40% of men and women have difficulty sleeping.) When the elderly change time zones, they are asking an already disrupted system to experience even greater upheaval, and then to adjust and stabilize. Eventually, jet lag will subside, but it will have taken an unusually severe toll. However, a hidden benefit of severe jet lag and the resultant reestablishment of a new body rhythm in a new time zone is often a sense of renewed vigor and a sudden ability to sleep through the night. For this reason, *The Cure for Jet Lag* and the 3-Step System can be very advantageous to the elderly. Through the 3-Step System, not only are jet lag symptoms reduced, but the system literally forces a resynchronization that might otherwise have eluded the elderly person for years, if not for the rest of his or her life.

Health Factors

Good Health versus Illness. If you are in ill health, jet lag may make you feel even worse. Sickness and disease cause their own disruption of body rhythms, and jet lag compounds the feeling of malaise. There is good evidence that disrupted body rhythms permit, encourage or even cause illness, particularly mental illness in the category of "affective disorders" and depression.

Drugs versus No Drugs. If you are taking prescription or nonprescription drugs, often the timing of these drugs is crucial to their working properly. When you change time zones, your body clock begins to adjust accordingly. As a result, drugs can temporarily lose their effectiveness or even end up having a detrimental effect, depending upon at what point they are taken during the twenty-four-hour day. At the University of Minnesota, the effectiveness of chemotherapy has been proved to depend significantly upon what time of day the drugs are administered.

Even such ubiquitous drugs as alcohol, nicotine, marijuana, and coffee cause changes in your biochemistry that disrupt your body rhythms throughout the day and night. Taken alone or in combination, they can worsen the problem of jet lag and retard jet lag recuperation.

All this means that it is very difficult to be specific about the length of time required to adapt to a new time zone. It depends upon:

1. How many time zones you have crossed.

2. Whether you have flown from west to east or from east to west.

3. What personality, social, age, and health factors are involved.

4. Whether you have employed any countermeasures, such as those described in *The Cure for Jet Lag* before, during, or after the trip.

Also, some people are better endowed genetically than others with flexible body clocks that can be readily reset, either forward or backward. Furthermore, in the course of a trip, some people inadvertently do all of the "wrong" things to counteract jet lag, while others, the lucky ones, accidentally hit upon the "right" things to reduce jet lag symptoms.

CHAPTER THREE

WHAT YOU NEED TO KNOW ABOUT TIME ZONES

Time Structure and the Planet Earth

In order to use *The Cure for Jet lag* and the 3-Step System, you need to understand time zones and how to calculate how many you will be crossing if you are flying east/west or west/east so you can choose the proper plan. Remember, if you are flying strictly north/south or south/north, you will not be changing time zones, no matter how far you fly or how many hours you are in the air. If you're going to have to reset your wristwatch upon arrival, you are changing time zones.

Briefly stated, by international agreement the world uses twenty-four standard meridians of longitude (imaginary lines on the earth's surface that run from the North Pole to the South Pole), to delineate the 24 time zones that comprise a day. The meridians are spaced fifteen degrees apart, and counting commences at the "prime" meridian running through Greenwich, England, where the time zone is known as Greenwich Mean Time.

In practice, the boundaries of some time zones zigzag for the convenience of local residents, and at the discretion of some city planners. For the most part, however, time is uniform throughout an individual time zone, and, with just a few exceptions, each time zone differs from the ones it borders by exactly an hour. During eastbound travel, the day shortens; that is, the clock must be set ahead for as many hours as the number of time zones that have been crossed. Conversely, during westbound travel, the clock has to be set back.

Take a look at the Mercator Map on the next page. The Mercator Map is a cylindrical map projection presented by the Flemish geographer and cartographer Gerardus Mercator in 1569. It became the standard map projection for nautical purposes because of its ability to represent lines of constant true bearing or true course. Of course, because it is impossible to represent accurately the spherical surface of the earth on a flat piece of paper, there is some distortion of size, but the individual time zones are clearly indicated and can be easily counted by hand. You can also find Web sites that will help you calculate time zone changes if you have

MERCATOR MAP—TIME ZONES OF THE WORLD

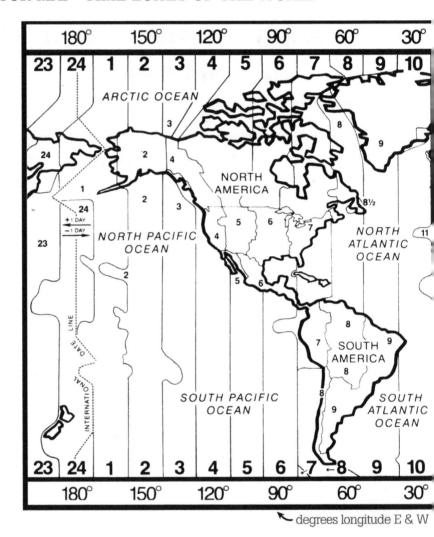

degrees longitude E & W

The Mercator map has been the standard navigation map for centuries. Because of its distinctive design, with polar regions exaggerated, it is an indispensable aid for jet travelers counting the number of time zone changes involved in flight.

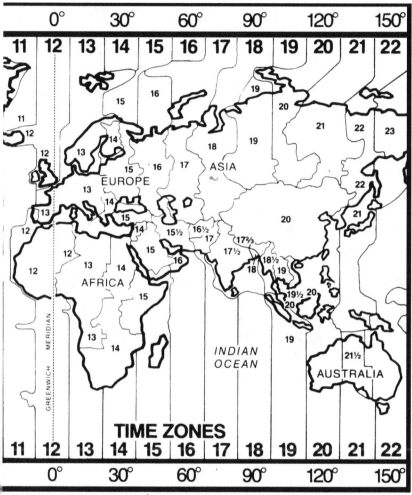

of Greenwich Meridian ➚

your computer or laptop handy. Just perform an online search for "world time clock" or "time zone calculator" and you'll find plenty of Web sites from which to choose.

Note also that there are some very exotic places highlighted on the maps in Chapter Seven and Chapter Eight, as representative of potential trips. Although it is much more likely that your transmeridional travels will take you from London to Zurich, from Edinburgh to Frankfurt, from Paris to Athens, or perhaps even from Oklahoma City to Philadelphia more frequently than from Nome to Papeete or from Pago Pago to Santa Maria in the Azores, exotic destinations were included on the sample sheets for far more than purely romantic reasons. The places chosen represent the best aids that were available within their respective times zones that would provide a broad perspective of round-the-world travel.

Differences Between Standard U.S. Time Zones and Foreign Countries

The following figure displays time zone changes from the United States ONLY to eighty different countries around the world. Determine whether the city from which you are departing the United States is on Eastern, Central, Mountain or Pacific Standard Time; then find your destination city along the left-hand column.

Differences Between
Standard U.S. Time Zones
and Foreign Countries

	Time Difference U.S. Time Zone			
	EST	CST	MST	PST
American Samoa	-6	-5	-4	-3
Andorra	6	7	8	9
Argentina	2	3	4	5
Australia	16	17	18	19
Austria	6	7	8	9
Bahrain	8	9	10	11
Belgium	6	7	8	9
Belize	-1	0	1	2
Bolivia	1	2	3	4
Brazil	2	3	4	5
Chile	2	3	4	5
Colombia	0	1	2	3
Costa Rica	-1	0	1	2
Cyprus	7	8	9	10
Denmark	6	7	8	9
Ecuador	0	1	2	3
El Salvador	-1	0	1	2
Fiji	17	18	19	20
Finland	7	8	9	10
France	6	7	8	9
French Antilles	1	2	3	4
Germany	6	7	8	9
Greece	7	8	9	10
Guam	15	16	17	18
Guatemala	-1	0	1	2
Guyana	2	3	4	5
Haiti	0	1	2	3

Differences Between Standard U.S. Time Zones and Foreign Countries

	Time Difference U.S. Time Zone			
	EST	CST	MST	PST
Honduras	-1	0	1	2
Hong Kong	13	14	15	16
Indonesia (Western)	12	13	14	15
Iran	8.5	9.5	10.5	11.5
Iraq	8	9	10	11
Ireland	5	6	7	8
Israel	7	8	9	10
Italy	6	7	8	9
Ivory Coast	5	6	7	8
Japan	14	15	16	17
Kenya	8	9	10	11
Korea	14	15	16	17
Kuwait	8	9	10	11
Liberia	5	6	7	8
Libya	6	7	8	9
Liechtenstein	6	7	8	9
Luxembourg	6	7	8	9
Malaysia	13	14	15	16
Monaco	6	7	8	9
Netherlands	6	7	8	9
Netherlands Antilles	1	2	3	4
New Caledonia	16	17	18	19
New Zealand	17	18	19	20
Nicaragua	-1	0	1	2
Nigeria	6	7	8	9
Norway	6	7	8	9
Panama	0	1	2	3
Papua New Guinea	15	16	17	18
Paraguay	1	2	3	4
Peru	0	1	2	3
Philippines	13	14	15	16

	Time Difference U.S. Time Zone			
	EST	CST	MST	PST
Portugal	5	6	7	8
Romania	7	8	9	10
Russia	8	9	10	11
San Marino	6	7	8	9
Saudi Arabia	8	9	10	11
Senegal	5	6	7	8
Serbia	6	7	8	9
Singapore	13	14	15	16
South Africa	7	8	9	10
Spain	6	7	8	9
Sri Lanka	10.5	11.5	12.5	13.5
Suriname	1.5	2.5	3.5	4.5
Sweden	6	7	8	9
Switzerland	6	7	8	9
Tahiti	-5	-4	-3	-2
Taiwan	13	14	15	16
Thailand	12	13	14	15
Tunisia	6	7	8	9
Turkey	8	9	10	11
United Arab Emirates	9	10	11	12
United Kingdom	5	6	7	8
Venezuela	1	2	3	4

Ribbons of Cities—Location of Landmark Cities According to World Time Zones

The Ribbons of Cities table that follows provides an extremely accurate reference to determine the north/south or east/west direction of flights. It is based strictly on longitude. Should your trip involve a significant east/west route, you must implement *The Cure for Jet Lag* in order to reduce dramatically or even eliminate jet lag symptoms . . . or you will pay the price. Don't want any jet lag at all? Fly a north/south or south/north route!

Ribbons of Cities

STD TIME ZONES IDL*	1h	2h	3h
STD TIME ZONES GMT**	-11h	-10h	-9h
	Western Alaska	Alaska-Hawaii	West Yukon
NAME OF TIME ZONE	WAST	AHST	WYST
APPROXIMATE*** BASIC			
LONGITUDE (W-E)	165°W	150°W	135°W

ARCTIC CIRCLE

Barrow

66.5°N LAT	Nome	Fairbanks	
	Dutch Harbor	Anchorage	

TROPIC OF CANCER

23.5°N LAT		Honolulu	

EQUATOR 0° LAT

	Pago Pago	Papeete L-	
	(Samoa)	(Tahiti)	

23.5° S LAT

TROPIC OF CAPRICORN

66.5°S LAT

ANTARCTIC CIRCLE

*Standard time zones 1-24, with reference to the International Date Line.
**Standard time zones 1-24, with reference to Greenwich Mean Time.

Location of Landmark Cities According to World Time Zones

4h	5h	6h
-8h	-7h	-6h
Pacific	Mountain	Central
PST	MST	CST
120°W	105°W	90°W
Juneau	Edmonton	Winnipeg
Vancouver	Calgary	Minneapolis
Seattle		Omaha
Portland	Salt Lake City	Chicago
San Francisco	Denver	Kansas City
Los Angeles	Phoenix	Dallas-Ft. Worth
San Diego		Houston
		New Orleans
		Mexico City
		Guatemala

***As discussed earlier, in some cases cities are in a time zone removed from the expected longitude, due to local preference: these are shown by L– or –L, symbolizing direction of the true longitude.

33

Ribbons of Cities

	7h	8h	9h
STD TIME ZONES IDL*			
STD TIME ZONES GMT**	−5h	−4h	−3h
	Eastern	Atlantic	Argentine
			E. Brazilian
NAME OF TIME ZONE	EST	AST	ABST
APPROXIMATE*** BASIC LONGITUDE (W-E)	75°W	60°W	45°W
		Sondre	
ARCTIC CIRCLE		Stromfjord	
66.5°N LAT	Montreal	Halifax	
	Toronto		
	Boston		
	Detroit		
	Cleveland		
	New York		
	Philadelphia		
	Washington-Baltimore		
	Atlanta		
	Tampa	Hamilton	
	Miami	(Bermuda)	
	Nassau		
TROPIC OF CANCER			
23.5°N LAT	Kingston	San Juan, P.R.	
	(Jamaica)	Caracas	
	Havana	Fort-de-France	
	Panama City	(Martinique)	
	Bogota		
EQUATOR 0° LAT			
	Quito	La Paz	Brasilia
	Lima		Rio de Janeiro
23.5° S LAT			
TROPIC OF CAPRICORN		Santiago	Sao Paolo
		de Chile	
			Montevideo
			Buenos Aires
66.5°S LAT			
ANTARCTIC CIRCLE			

*Standard time zones 1-24, with reference to the International Date Line.
**Standard time zones 1-24, with reference to Greenwich Mean Time.

Location of Landmark Cities According to World Time Zones

10h	11h	12h
-2h	-1h	0h
Midatlantic	Azores	Greenwich
MAST	AST	GMT
30°W	15°W	0°
	Scoresbysund	
	(Greenland)	
		Reykjavik
	Santa Maria	London
	(Azores)	Dublin
		Lisbon
		Casablanca
		Algiers
		Los Palmas
		(Canary Islands)
		Dakar
		Accra
Fernando		
de Noronha (Brazil)		

***As discussed earlier, in some cases cities are in a time zone removed from the expected longitude, due to local preference: these are shown by L– or –L, symbolizing direction of the true longitude.

Ribbons of Cities

	13h	14h	15h
STD TIME ZONES IDL*	+1h	+2h	+3h
STD TIME ZONES GMT**	Central	Balkan Egypt	Moscow-Arabia
			E. Africa
NAME OF TIME ZONE	CET	BEST	MEAT
APPROXIMATE*** BASIC			
LONGITUDE (W-E)	15°E	30°E	45°E

ARCTIC CIRCLE			Murmansk
66.5°N LAT	Oslo	Helsinki	St. Petersburg
	Stockholm	Bucharest	Moscow
	Copenhagen	Sofia	Kiev
	Berlin	Athens	Ankara
	Warsaw	Beirut	Istanbul
	Amsterdam	Tel Aviv	Baghdad
	Brussels	Cairo	Kuwait
	Luxembourg		Dhahran
	Frankfurt, Prague		
	Paris, Munich		
	Vienna, Geneva		
	Zurich		
	Milan		
	Rome, Belgrade		
	Madrid		
	Tunis		
TROPIC OF CANCER			
23.5°N LAT	Lagos	Khartoum	Jiddah
			Addis Ababa
EQUATOR 0° LAT	Brazzaville		Nairobi
			Dar es Salaam
23.5° S LAT			
TROPIC OF CAPRICORN		Johannesburg	
		Cape Town	
66.5°S LAT			
ANTARCTIC CIRCLE			

*Standard time zones 1-24, with reference to the International Date Line.
**Standard time zones 1-24, with reference to Greenwich Mean Time.

Location of Landmark Cities According to World Time Zones

16h	17h	18h
+4h	+5h	+6h
Baku-Abu Dhabi	Karachi	Omsk
BAT	KT	OT
60°E	75°E	90°E

Kazan	Sverdlovsk	Omsk
Volgograd	Delhi 5 ½	Tashkent
Baku	Karachi	
Teheran 3 ½ Abu Dhabi		
Kabul 4 ½		

Calcutta 5 ½	
Bombay 5 ½	
Colombo 5 ½	Yangon 6 ½
	(Rangoon)

***As discussed earlier, in some cases cities are in a time zone removed from the expected longitude, due to local preference: these are shown by L– or –L, symbolizing direction of the true longitude.

Ribbons of Cities

STD TIME ZONES IDL*	19h	20h	21h
STD TIME ZONES GMT**	+7h	+8h	+9h
	Bangkok	Beijing	Japan Standard
		Shanghai	
NAME OF TIME ZONE	BT	CST	JST
APPROXIMATE*** BASIC			
LONGITUDE (W–E)	105°E	120°E	135°E

ARCTIC CIRCLE

66.5°N LAT	Novosibirsk	Irkutsk	
		Beijing	
		Lhasa	Tokyo
		Shanghai	Seoul

TROPIC OF CANCER

23.5°N LAT	Bangkok	Hong Kong	
		Manila	
		Singapore	

EQUATOR 0° LAT

Jakarta

23.5° S LAT

TROPIC OF CAPRICORN   Perth

66.5°S LAT

ANTARCTIC CIRCLE

*Standard time zones 1-24, with reference to the International Date Line.
**Standard time zones 1-24, with reference to Greenwich Mean Time.

Location of Landmark Cities According to World Time Zones

22h	23h	24h
+10h	+11h	+12h
Sydney	Truk	New Zealand
Melbourne		
SMT	TT	NZT
150°W	165°W	180°W
		Kamchatsky
Vladivostok		
Guam	Truk	Wake
Darwin 9 ½ Port	Noumea	Fiji
Moresby	(New Caledonia)	
Adelaide 9 ½ Sydney		Auckland
Melbourne		Wellington

***As discussed earlier, in some cases cities are in a time zone removed from the expected longitude, due to local preference: these are shown by L– or –L, symbolizing direction of the true longitude.

CHAPTER FOUR

TRICKING BODY CLOCKS TO A NEW TIME ZONE

Old Remedies versus *The Cure for Jet Lag*

Many people simply do not have the luxury of allowing jet lag to diminish gradually over a period of days or weeks. Sometimes the duration of a trip is only a day or two, or a week, and jet lag symptoms can take so long to subside naturally that you may well be on your way home or about to take off for yet another destination before you have fully adjusted to the new time zone in which you have landed.

In particular, the problem of jet lag concerns men and women who, for a variety of reasons, must be mentally sharp and/or physically fit almost, if not immediately, upon arrival. Often these people are diplomats who must negotiate sensitive issues with far-reaching implications; or athletes whose competitors include not only others suffering from jet lag, but local athletes at their peak of physical prowess; or business people for whom a convention or a specific meeting may be absolutely crucial to success or failure. For these people, uncontrolled jet lag presents a very serious situation.

Over the course of the years, however, a few home remedies have evolved, some no more than nonsensical or counterproductive, others more successful and useful because they accidentally incorporate helpful techniques. None, however, are as effective as *The Cure for Jet Lag*.

The first remedy involves preflight adjustment over a period of days before departure:

1. The Henry Kissinger Approach. When former Secretary of State Henry Kissinger knew he had to attend an important meeting in a foreign country, in the hope that he could systematically shift his body clocks to foreign time before he actually boarded the airplane, he would try to retire one hour earlier each night and rise one hour later.

Did it work? The problem with the Kissinger approach to "shuttle diplomacy" is that the demands of public and private life at home and before departure seldom permit the kind of rigid commitment and self-discipline this technique entails. Not only is it extremely difficult, as well as impractical, to withdraw so totally from daily events, it is actually impossible to remain unaffected physiologically by environmental influences such as the light/dark patterns and the social cues around you.

If the technique worked at all, it did not work well. From the studies performed on phase shifts associated with body clock changes, in all likelihood Kissinger experienced nearly as much jet lag on the first day at each of his destinations as the person who had sat next to him in the airplane.

The second approach involves arriving several days ahead of time when an important appointment, meeting, or event is scheduled:

2. The Dwight D. Eisenhower Approach. In 1955, President Eisenhower flew into Geneva on a Friday for a summit meeting with Nikita Khrushchev the following Monday. Eisenhower had arrived early in order to try to reduce his jet lag symptoms in time for the meeting.

Was Eisenhower successful in reducing his jet lag symptoms? Partially, but not totally. Studies on jet lag symptoms indicate that recuperation actually does take about a day (more or less) per time zone through which the traveler has flown. Had Eisenhower arrived in Geneva an entire week prior to the summit meeting, he would have been well on his way to recovery, but in the absence of the other jet lag countermeasures discussed later, just two or three days are ordinarily not enough time for full adjustment to the new time zone. In fact, Eisenhower was still very much in a state of cellular upheaval, although his sleeping/waking patterns may have begun to synchronize with local time.

As an interesting note, in the past, companies such as Continental Oil Company and Phillips Petroleum Company (now CONOCO-Phillips, Inc.) actually insisted that their executives use a modified Eisenhower approach and take one full day to adjust from easterly trips before resuming business-oriented activities. However, as in-depth studies have indicated, jet lag begins from the moment the plane lands and continues for days thereafter whenever a time zone change has occurred.

The third approach to jet lag is to adhere rigorously to your own hometown schedule, no matter where you are in the world:

3. The Lyndon Johnson Approach. President Johnson rarely, if ever, reset his wristwatch when Air Force One landed in a foreign country. When he flew to Guam to confer with President Nguyen Van Thieu of South Vietnam, Johnson remained on his usual time schedule, eating when he would have at the White House, sleeping when it was dark in Washington, D.C., and arranging meetings at his convenience during what were reasonable hours in the United States.

Was Johnson's technique effective? To a degree, yes, but his approach required an iron will and total denial of events transpiring around him. If you are interested in experiencing the country you are visiting by dining out, by touring its museums, etc., forcing yourself to remain on hometown time will put you totally out of sync with everyone else and everyone else's schedule.

If you schedule a meeting at what might be the middle of the night at your destination, but only afternoon by your hometown schedule, will you be more alert? Yes, and perhaps you can get away with it if you are the President of the United States—but chances are other members of the meeting may not be willing to adjust their entire schedules to accommodate you.

The fourth way to control jet lag involves the systematic and orderly introduction of environmental cues and other agents that predictably influence body clocks. These include illumination, exercise, social cues, foods that encourage sleep, and common beverages that contain natural chemicals.

4. *The Cure for Jet Lag* 3-Step System Approach. Beginning from one to three days prior to flight (depending on how much notice you have to implement the 3-Step System before your plane takes off), *The Cure for Jet Lag* continues for the day of the flight, and for the first few days at your destination.

Will it be more effective than the other three approaches? Absolutely! And:

- You will initiate the resetting and resynchronization of those body clocks that may have been disturbed prior to your actual trip.

- You will not have to readjust your waking and sleeping patterns while at home using the "Kissinger" technique for days prior to flight.

- You will not have to waste valuable vacation or business time recuperating for days from jet lag in a foreign hotel.

- You will be better able to function from the moment you land because the system forces you to step right into the mainstream of activity.
- You will feel fine before, during, and after your trip.

Finally, being informed about the basic causes and symptoms of jet lag and circadian dyschronism, you are better equipped to deal with and to prevent the onset of similar problems and disorders in your daily living even when you are not engaged in global travel.

Origins of *The Cure for Jet Lag* 3-Step System

For hundreds of years, researchers have studied a variety of the rhythms present in the universe and on earth, but only in the past few decades have scientists become concerned with how to force the rhythms of human body clocks ahead or back.

Years ago, with few exceptions, the need to alter body clocks simply did not exist. Life was lived mostly in synchronization with the rhythms of nature. With the advent of candles, kerosene lamps, and, eventually, electric lights, these rhythms could be ignored to some extent, but generally speaking, as members of a rural society, people stuck to the daytime (or diurnal) patterns and left the nights to the owls, bats, and other nocturnal creatures of the earth.

World war, twenty-four-hour security watches, around-the-clock assembly line work, and varying work shifts for doctors, nurses, firemen, policemen, etc., began to turn night into day, and workers started to try to buck the daytime genetic programming of millions of years of evolution. The result was greatly diminished mental acuity, enormous reduction in physical prowess that changed "sure win" to "sure lose," significant increases in errors and inefficiency, and the production of such overwhelming fatigue that workers often fell asleep on the job.

The challenge fell to scientists and researchers who, often with laboratory animals, but sometimes with humans as well, began not only to establish what normal daytime rhythms were, but also to try to determine ways to help turn a daytime creature into a nighttime animal, so that work could be performed more efficiently, and the number of problems associated with "shift work" could be eliminated or reduced. Thus, the goal initially had nothing to do with jet travel, though it would turn out that the search for an aid to shift workers would pay dividends a few decades later, once jet lag arrived on the scene.

The simpler studies were performed on animals under controlled conditions in laboratories. Some important preliminary research suggested that, since the daily rhythms of all body functions fluctuate in patterns throughout a twenty-four hour day, body temperature (which is higher in the day and lower at night) could provide one of the easiest and clearest indications of when body rhythms were in a state of transition and when they had finally assumed a daytime pattern during nighttime hours. Because temperature was known to be one of the last functions to adapt to a time shift, it was safe to assume that when temperature had stabilized, all other body rhythms had adapted as well.

Once scientists were confident that they knew how many hours, days, and weeks were involved in the natural smoothing of disrupted body rhythms after a time shift, they were able to move on to an even more challenging aspect of body clocks—how to accelerate the shift artificially.

Major Influences on Body Clocks

Light/Dark Phases, Food, Social Cues. Working with laboratory animals and humans, scientists first considered external factors that appeared to activate or deactivate the body's clocks. Although now there is a whole laundry list of known influences on body clocks, initially only two were identified. These *zeitgebers* (pronounced tsight-gaybers, from the German for "time-givers") were the sunlight/darkness cue that "told" the man or animal when it was time to wake or when it was time to sleep, and the food cue that stimulated eating and thereby the resupply of energy reserves. However, a third cue, which influenced alertness and wakefulness, was subsequently discovered.

This additional cue involved "social" triggers: the schedule of when the person or animal was accustomed to getting up (whether by an alarm clock going off or having a laboratory technician turn the light switch on); when normally it would be time for performing daytime tasks (working a job or running a maze); and when typically there would be interaction with others (conversing with family in the evening or keeping contact until the technician turned out the lights). We now know that social cues include all sorts of interpersonal interaction, such as eating together rather than alone, intense intellectual activity, homework, reading, writing—in short, anything that involves mental stimulation.

Timing. Knowing that a phase shift is essentially a body-wide biochemical

45

event, chronobiologists took the investigation yet another step. They discovered two facts. The first is that your entire body chemistry changes over the course of a day. Quite literally you are a different person biochemically at six in the morning than you are at midnight, so much so that it is the equivalent of being a redhead at dawn and a blond at midnight. The second fact is that because of this constant inconstancy within you, your body chemistry reacts quite differently at different times of the day to the same stimulus, ranging from not reacting at all to reacting as expected, to reacting as if under acute stress.

Consider, for example, daylight as a cue to help set the body's timers and keep them synchronized. How pleasant it is, how reinforcing to a sense of personal well-being, to soak up the sun's rays on a sunny beach. Mankind accepts light and takes pleasure in its presence during the active phase of his daily cycle, but rejects it and finds it abhorrent if it suddenly flashes on at 3 AM during his inactive phase. In humans, daytime exercise in the form of jogging, tennis, handball, swimming, or aerobic dancing are invigorating and positive reinforcers of body clocks during daytime activity, but are genuinely stressful when they take place in the dead of night.

Natural Chemicals. Scientists then extended their search to drugs, man-made as well as natural, and into chemicals that might be combined with the known cues (light/dark, food, and "social") to affect biological rhythms. In the process scientists discovered that a variety of chemicals, including those found quite naturally in beverages people were drinking every day, such as coffee or tea, could act "chronobiologically." This is to say, depending on when and how quickly they were consumed, certain beverages could dramatically speed up or slow down body clocks.

The following chart, labeled "Major Influences on Body Clocks," lists in more detail the cues that scientists have determined have an impact on biological rhythms. *The Cure for Jet Lag* 3-Step System integrates all (except the items listed under "Drugs") into a simple yet comprehensive strategy for overcoming jet lag.

Major Influences on Body Clocks	

Light and dark
  Sunlight
  Electric lights
  Window blinds
	Methylated xanthines
	  Caffeine
	  Theophylline
	  Theobromine

Food
  Proteins
  Carbohydrates
  Fats
	Drugs
	  Antihypertensives
	  Tranquilizers
	  Sleeping pills
	  Hallucinogens

Physical activity Mental activity	Social Interactions

Suddenly, researchers began to put it all together in their search for aid to night workers. Just as suddenly, researchers began to recognize that the information they discovered applied not only to shift workers, but also to people suffering from jet lag, since the cause of both had their origins in changing body clock rhythms and massive disruptions of sense of time, place, and well-being.

CHAPTER FIVE

HOW *THE CURE FOR JET LAG* WORKS

The 3-Step System

The Cure for Jet Lag is divided into three steps that coincide with the three phases of your flight:

Preflight

Inflight

Postflight

The 3-Step System integrates all the knowledge scientists have gathered about rephasing body clocks ahead or backward—100% naturally—through the combined use of the major external influences that are known to have a positive impact on the timing of body clocks: patterns of light and darkness, certain foods, periods of physical and mental activity, and naturally occurring chemicals found in coffee or tea.

How does the system work? The 3-Step System begins with the **Preflight Step** in which coffee and tea are temporarily eliminated and a period of feasting and fasting begins as you approach the day of your flight.[1] (Fasting here just means eating lightly and sparingly—or about 40-60% fewer calories than you would normally consume.) It progresses to the **Inflight Step**, where you begin to reset your body's internal time clocks from the old time zone to the new time zone while on board the plane through the use of coffee and tea, periods of light and darkness, and periods of quiet or activity. And it concludes after you land with the **Postflight Step**, when you eat meals that are designed to see that you get the biggest boost of dependable energy possible during the day while you are in a new time zone, and the best possible sleep at night.

It sounds simple because it is simple. By following the instructions in *The Cure for Jet Lag* you function optimally at home (during the Preflight Steps), feel

---

[1] If you suffer from withdrawal symptoms when you stop drinking coffee or tea (headache, backache, mental confusion, fatigue), in Chapter Ten you will find an over-the-counter remedy that doctors have found can greatly reduce or even eliminate your withdrawal symptoms.

comfortable on the airplane (during the Inflight Steps), and join the mainstream of activity as soon as you land (during the Postflight Steps), all with minimal effort.

Overcoming Jet Lag with Light and Dark

Whether you are fast asleep under a pile of blankets in a room with the shades down, or snug in a sleeping bag while camped out under the stars, when the lamp goes on or dawn breaks, like it or not you begin to enter the active phase of your twenty-four hour daytime cycle. In fact, all diurnal (daytime) animals on earth, including humans, react when light strikes the eye, which stimulates neurotransmitters, sending an immediate signal to specific regions of the brain. In turn, these brain regions notify the rest of the body that the awake and active phase is about to begin.

Man has tampered with the timing of the natural response to dawn and dusk, but without much success. Even using darkened rooms and artificial light, scientists have been able to alter the onset and duration of the active phase only marginally. Despite his best efforts, man remains a daytime animal locked into the signals and timing of light.

The problem with rapid air travel is that a long-distance flight involves a time frame change that forces the wake/sleep cycle to which you've become habituated to shift accordingly. And it will, in due course. Old rhythms die hard, however. In the interim you will feel the strong tug of sleep when your day would have ended back home and, try though you might to resist, your body will want to rise when you normally would have back home. This problem has the potential to persist for days or weeks, disrupting your waking and sleeping patterns, making you fatigued when everyone else at your destination is wide-eyed, and keeping you awake when the locals are retiring.

One of the keys, therefore, in *The Cure for Jet Lag* is to use natural and artificial light to help reset your wake/sleep schedule to the new time frame. You do this in two of the three steps: while in the airplane and from the moment you arrive at your destination.

How? By tricking your body into thinking that you've already arrived at your destination. For example, you should pull down the shade of a window seat while on board the plane during what would be nighttime at your destination—even if it is still daytime on your hometown schedule—or cover your eyes with an eyeshade or dark sunglasses to achieve the same effect.

Conversely, if your flight is at night but it's currently daytime at your destination, you can begin to **trick** your body into thinking it is already in the new time zone by turning on the plane's reading light over your seat during what would be daylight hours at your destination and resisting the temptation to doze off by disciplining yourself to read a book, do work on your computer, or watch the inflight movie.

Similarly, it's very important after you land not to succumb to your body's urge to sleep on your old time schedule. If it is daytime when you arrive, sequestering yourself in a darkened hotel room will only negate the benefits of *The Cure for Jet Lag*. Instead, you must expose yourself to local daylight (or artificial light, if you must remain indoors) to help prod your body into resetting its internal clock. Similarly, if you arrive at night, assume the destination schedule by immediately proceeding to your room, turning off the lights and shutting your eyes until dawn, sleeping as best you can. Soon enough, sleep will take over.

Your motto must be to *"live as the Romans live"* from the moment you arrive at your destination. If you are outdoors, flood your eyes with daylight. No sunglasses. If you are indoors during daytime, keep the artificial lights on. By saturating yourself in light at the appropriate times, you will be stimulating your diurnal/daylight neurotransmitters and hormones to begin their proper course through you at the proper time. In short order, fatigue will lift.

Overcoming Jet Lag with Specific Foods

Fatigue coupled with insomnia is the major complaint associated with jet lag. You become so tired that you cannot enjoy the local sights or function up to par during the daytime. Yet, despite exhaustion, a sound night's sleep eludes you. *The Cure for Jet Lag* offers a number of excellent methods that will help you fall asleep or keep you energized. One of these methods involves the intentional selection of certain foods to induce sleep or produce wakefulness.

Like everyone else, your state of sleepiness or wakefulness results from chemical changes in your brain that help "rev you up" or "slow you down" over the course of twenty-four hours. We've already noted the contribution made by light and darkness, but in addition, two complementary chemical pathways exist that accelerate and decelerate at different times of the diurnal cycle.

Overcoming Jet Lag with Specific Foods

During daytime hours various natural chemicals and chemical reactions occuring in your body's adrenalin (or catecholamine) pathway stimulate the billions of cells within your brain and in all other organic systems in your body. Chemical activity along the adrenalin pathway insures that you *will* be active during the active phase of your day. In contrast, at night, the reactions of the adrenalin pathway yield to another series of chemical combinations, these involving tryptophan and serotonin and called the indoleamine pathway. The indoleamine pathway begins a sleep-inducing process that makes you drowsy and, ultimately, puts you to sleep. Both pathways, by the way, are the targets of action for a variety of drugs, including antihypertensives. psychotropics, sleeping pills, tranquilizers, analgesics, and anesthetics. More on that later.

Researchers have shown that a meal composed primarily of high-protein foods such as fish, fowl, eggs, meat, dairy products or beans, stimulates the adrenalin pathway, providing up to five hours' worth of long-lasting energy. However, a meal consisting principally of high-carbohydrate foods, such as bread, pasta, rice, corn, oats, potatoes, salad, fruit, and rich desserts, while providing an initial surge of energy that lasts for up to an hour, thereafter influences the indoleamine pathway, provoking the urge to go to sleep.

By exploiting your knowledge of the competing effects of these two pathways, you can boost your body's ability to adapt to radical time changes. For instance, if you arrive in Austria in the morning after a long flight from the United States through many time zones and indulge in a breakfast of sugar-coated cereal and a sugar-sweetened beverage (all very high in carbohydrates), you can expect within the hour to become fatigued and want to lie down—which is, of course, exactly the wrong thing to do. If, instead, you eat a hearty breakfast of steak and eggs, or an omelet, lean sausage, cheese and milk (all of which are very high in protein), you'll be stimulating your body's active cycle. Taking the high-protein meal one step further, if you later have a high-protein lunch that includes lean beef, quiche (cheese), or fish and milk, and avoid carbohydrates, you will virtually guarantee an entire day of sustained energy. Then, if in the evening you consume a high-carbohydrate selection of pasta, vegetarian salad and bread followed by a rich dessert, thereby avoiding or at least minimizing your protein intake, you will be preparing yourself, on a biochemical level, for sleep.

All that is required is the ability to sort out a menu (just ask the waiter to translate, if necessary), or to do your own shopping with high-protein breakfasts and lunches and high-carbohydrate suppers in mind.

Does this technique involve a great deal of self-discipline? Not if you realize that you are not really being denied any food during a particular day, but are simply postponing some favorite foods. Ideally, you should continue the high protein breakfasts and lunches and high carbohydrate dinners throughout the course of your trip.

As is dramatically evident in the illustration below, a high-protein breakfast (eggs, lean meat or fish, dairy products) sustains blood sugar energy throughout the morning. A high-carbohydrate breakfast (bread, doughnuts, sugar) results in immediate energy but leads to a rapid and drastic decline in blood sugar within an hour of breakfast. The effect of a high-fat breakfast is intermediate. (Adapted from Dr. Raymond Greene, Human Hormones. London, 1970, p. 232.)

Effects of Various Classes of Food on Blood Sugar Level

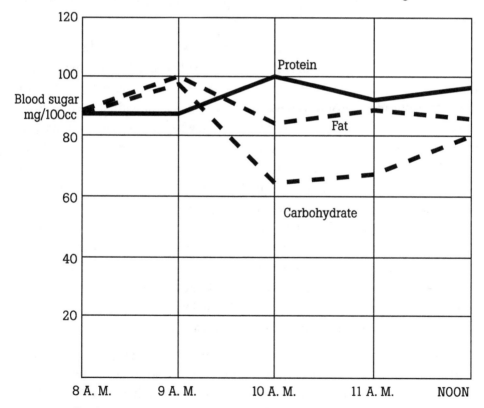

For the air traveler, high-protein breakfasts and lunches and high–carbohydrate dinners should be **de rigueur**, and anything else **verboten**.

Yes, you must forego the "continental breakfast" of croissants or muffins slathered in jelly that is the customary fare at many hotels (and you should keep that in mind when making hotel arrangements). Nor is the typical American breakfast of grapefruit, sugar-coated cereal, sugar-sweetened orange drink and toast, or syrup-saturated pancakes or French toast a good idea—although you certainly can have any of these items toward evening. Your strategy should be to eat greasy french fries, mayonnaise, ketchup, and the like only sparingly during the day, waiting for evening to indulge in all those foods you denied yourself earlier. Treat yourself to a huge pasta meal (hold the meat) at night and as much wine and liquor as is sensible in the late afternoon and early evening. With this regimen you can expect to draw on more than enough energy during the day, and then, as the evening winds down, you will wind down too.

Overcoming Jet Lag with Carefully Timed Coffee or Tea

Controlling your exposure to light and intelligently choosing what to eat are but two aspects of *The Cure for Jet Lag*. There's another.

In experiments with laboratory animals, scientists discovered a revolutionary fact with important implications: because the biochemistry of the body changes so radically over the course of a twenty-four hour day (the blond to redhead syndrome as described previously), individual chemicals can induce different bodily responses depending on where in the daily activity cycle they occur. Specifically, when chemicals known as "methylated xanthines" were administered to laboratory animals during early portions of their active phase, the animals' average temperature dropped and their body functions slowed to levels characteristic of nighttime. Amazingly, when these same methylated xanthines were administered late in the active phase, once again there was a dramatic reaction, only this time the body functions altered to that of a much *later* hour. (Interestingly, when the methylated xanthines were introduced in mid-afternoon, very little effect on body clocks occurred.) Thus it would appear that through the timely introduction of methylated xanthines, body clocks can be reset either forward or backward, more or less at will.

Of course, this discovery has huge implications for dealing with jet lag. After all, what are we trying to do if not to stop our body clocks cold and reset them forward or backward? But, where in the world can we get our hands on methylated xanthines? Do we need a prescription?

No. Three readily available methylated xanthines are *theophylline* and *theobromine*, both of which are found naturally in many teas, and *caffeine*, which is found in tea and coffee.

So you will not be surprised to learn that coffee and tea play a significant role in *The Cure for Jet Lag*. These natural chemicals, for those people who can tolerate them,[2] offer another mechanism for dramatically mitigating jet lag symptoms. Through their ability to affect simultaneously the billions of cells in each of the major organic systems of the body, these chemicals can help you rapidly resynchronize your hometown body clock to another time zone, enabling you to cut days and even weeks off the impact of jet lag.

There is only one slight hitch to the use of these chemicals: *in order for methylated xanthines to be most effective, you must give them up for a short time prior to your trip—up to three days—and then time their reintroduction and continued use carefully.* But don't worry. If you drink so much coffee or tea that you fear withdrawal symptoms, there's a proven all-natural over-the-counter remedy. This antidote to withdrawal symptoms will help relieve the headache, backache, fatigue, etc., that coffee and tea drinkers are all too familiar with when they try to "kick the habit." You'll be initiating a special, but easy, feast/fast ("fast" meaning eat lightly) meal pattern before the flight to set the stage for the moment *The Cure for Jet Lag* calls for you to reintroduce methylated xanthines into your system.

By the way, methylated xanthines should be taken in a "punctuate" (i.e., quick and timely) fashion. The exact time of day you take them will vary according to the direction in which you are traveling and the number of time zones you will be crossing. More on that later.

While this part of *The Cure for Jet Lag* requires a certain amount of will power, properly controlling and timing your intake of methylated xanthines is crucial to your success. Throughout the preflight, inflight, and postflight steps of *The Cure for Jet Lag*, the high-protein breakfasts and lunches, and high-carbohydrate suppers that you eat will help insure energy throughout the

---

[2] If you simply cannot tolerate coffee or tea, even just during the 3-Step System, don't drink the coffee or tea. Proceed with the other aspects of the 3-Step System. An inability to drink coffee or tea does not mean the rest of the 3-Step System will not help you overcome jet lag quickly.

An Over-the-Counter Remedy for Caffeine Withdrawal

The Cure for Jet Lag calls for abstaining from coffee or tea from one to three days before flight, followed by a blast of carefully-timed coffee or tea later on, to help trick your body clock into a new time zone. If you are among the people who have severe caffeine withdrawal symptoms, don't worry. *The Cure for Jet Lag* **recommends an over-the-counter remedy that doctors have found will reduce or eliminate withdrawal symptoms.** You'll be surprised to find out what that simple remedy is. It works! And it's Alka Seltzer® Gold!

According to Marshall Mandell M. D. , co-author of the best-seller *5-Day Allergy Relief System*, if you are experiencing withdrawal symptoms, it will help to "take two tablets of Alka Seltzer Gold with two glasses of water: one tablet in each 8-ounce glass." Do not take the regular Alka Seltzer because it contains aspirin. If you read the Alka Seltzer Gold label, you'll see it contains sodium bicarbonate and potassium bicarbonate with a few other ingredients. *Warning: ask a doctor before use if you have kidney disease or a potassium or sodium restricted diet. If you are pregnant or breast feeding ask a heath professional before use.*

By the way, decaffeinated coffee and tea are fine at any time.

If You Cannot Tolerate Caffeine in Any Form

For those people who simply cannot abide drinking black coffee or strong, plain tea, even a few quick cups, just follow all the other instructions in *The Cure for Jet Lag* and you'll be fine. The 3-Step System is a "combination punch" of jet lag fighting tactics. One missing element won't negate the benefits of the other steps that constitute the 3-Step System.

day and a restful sleep at night, while the proper timing of theophylline, caffeine or theobromine in coffee or tea will reduce the major trauma to your body clocks that time frame shifts produce.

Products Containing Methylated Xanthines. While most people think coffee is the major source of caffeine, it is also found in large quantities in soft drinks, tea, and other products. In order to help you avoid caffeinated products as you prepare for your flight, four major categories of caffeine-containing products are listed below. A more comprehensive list, which includes hundreds of drinks from A&W Cream Soda to Bazza High Energy Tea to ZipFizz Energy Drink Mix, as well as Haagen-Daz Coffee Ice Cream and Hershey's Chocolate Bars, can be found in the Appendix.

Coffee. How much caffeine coffee contains depends on how it is brewed, how long it is brewed, and whether it is regular or instant coffee. As a rule, brewed coffee contains about twice as much caffeine as instant coffee. The drip method of brewing results in a higher caffeine content than the percolator method.

Tea. The theophylline and caffeine content in tea depends on the type of tea leaves and the strength of the brew. If left to brew five minutes, for example, a cup of tea may have up to twice the caffeine equivalent of a cup that was brewed for one minute. As a rule, one cup of tea will have about one-fourth to one-third the caffeine equivalent of a cup of brewed coffee.

Chocolate. The cocoa bean contains natural theobromine. Theobromine content ranges from one to twenty milligrams per serving and has an average content of ten milligrams per serving.

Over-the-Counter Drugs. Many drugs contain significant amounts of caffeine. Stimulants such as NoDoz and Vivarin are the equivalent of one or two cups of coffee. Pain relief, weight control, and water-loss drugs can also contain large doses of caffeine.

Caffeine Content of Substances

Product	Quantity	Caffeine (in milligrams)
Coffee		
Decaffeinated	5 oz.	2
Instant, regular	5 oz.	53
Percolated	5 oz.	110
Drip	5 oz.	146
Tea		
One-minute brew	5 oz.	9-33
Three-minute brew	5 oz.	20-46
Five-minute brew	5 oz.	20-50
Canned iced tea	12 oz.	22-36
Cocoa and chocolate		
Milk chocolate	1 oz.	6
Cocoa beverage (water mix)	6 oz.	10
Baking chocolate	1 oz.	35
Non-prescription drugs		
Stimulants		
Caffedrine® Capsules	standard dose	200
NoDoz® Tablets	standard dose	200
Vivarin® Tablets	standard dose	200
Pain relievers		
Anacin®	standard dose	0
Midol®	standard dose	64
Excedrin®	standard dose	65
Vanquish®	standard dose	130
Diuretics		
Pre-Mens Forte®	standard dose	100
Aqua-Ban®	standard dose	200
Cold remedies		
Coryban-D®	standard dose	30
Triaminicin®	standard dose	30
Dristan®	standard dose	30
Weight control aids		
Dietac®	daily dose	200
Dexatrim®	daily dose	200
Prolamine®	daily dose	140
Appedrine®	daily dose	100

Overcoming Jet Lag with High and Low Calorie Meals

As many of us learned in high school biology class, the chemical glycogen provides fuel to the human body. Normally, reserve levels of glycogen stored in the liver ebb and flow in response to food intake: glycogen in the liver and muscles peaks shortly after a meal and then tapers off steadily until the next time food is consumed. Of significance to jet lag sufferers, experiments have shown that if glycogen reserves are allowed to run low through fasting or eating sparingly, the body clock becomes especially sensitive to the effects of light, darkness, food and methylated xanthines. For example, laboratory rats allowed to eat at will and then exposed to a new lighting regimen corresponding to an eight-hour time frame delay—the equivalent of flying from Tokyo to Zaire, for example—took four to six days to resynchronize naturally. In contrast, laboratory rats denied food for the 24 hours prior to the time frame change, but then fed at the equivalent of breakfast time in Zaire, underwent a much more rapid shift to the new time frame.

What's more, glycogen provides yet another benefit to *The Cure for Jet Lag*: The impact of methylated xanthines is amplified when glycogen reserves are low. In other words, not only can you manipulate glycogen levels to good effect, but in the process you are enhancing the potency of other chemicals useful for resetting your body clock.

The obvious conclusion is that manipulating glycogen levels has a role to play in the 3-Step System. *The Cure for Jet Lag* integrates what scientists have learned about the impact of feasting and fasting (eating lightly), methylated xanthines, and the sudden appearance of food after a fast, into a comprehensive attack on jet lag symptoms.

Within the 3-Step System you assume an on-again/off-again pattern of feasting and fasting from one to three days prior to your trip, depending upon how many time zones you will change and how much advance notice you have of the flight. *The Cure for Jet Lag* feast/fast step repeatedly replenishes the glycogen supply and then drains it, biochemically setting the stage for your body clocks to shift to a new time frame rapidly.

Overcoming Jet Lag with Physical and Mental Activity

In most living creatures, light is the fundamental time-setter and reinforcer of body clocks. Man, however, is the exception to the rule. While light plays a powerful role in establishing or changing daily body rhythms, so do the effects of forced physical and mental activity. Having to get up and get out, whether to perform in a ballet or to catch a bus, actually causes chemical changes in the body that relate to stress and to the stimulation of unique neurotransmitters that help to keep you alert. Speaking to other people, socializing with them and "rubbing elbows" also precipitates the secretion of additional neurotransmitters that help body clocks resynchronize to a new time frame. Physically moving about, going to tour Versailles or the Kremlin, riding the Colorado rapids, or skiing in the Alps, even if you are in a different time frame, will shake you out of lethargy and help resynchronize your body clocks to the active phase.

With *The Cure for Jet Lag* the active phase is just that—active. If you are on the plane during what should be the active phase of *The Cure for Jet Lag*, read, write, talk to your neighbor, stretch, and move about. When you arrive at your destination, even though you might feel a strong urge to slow down because your body clocks are in transition, if your program calls for activity, keep walking and talking to help coerce your out-of-synchronization body clocks into speeding up the resynchronization process.

Between 1975 and 1981, in a number of scientific papers from laboratories around the world, the Preflight, Inflight, and Postflight steps involved in influencing body clocks were revealed, and the basis of *The Cure for Jet Lag* was established. By incorporating the use of light and darkness, a specific composition of foods, periods of physical and mental activity, and methylated xanthines found in coffee or tea with a feast/fast regimen, scientists showed that multiple factors influencing body clocks could, indeed, have dramatic impact on the severity and duration of jet lag-like symptoms.

It took over thirty years of research on national and international levels ultimately to amass all the disparate information and organize it into *The Cure for Jet Lag*, a system of relief that really works for the air traveler's most frequent complaint—jet lag.

In the pages that follow, the specific techniques you will use will be based on the direction of your flight and the number of hours you will need to reset your watch, either ahead or back, when you arrive at your destination. It will not matter how many airplanes you have to take to get where you are going, or whether you take off late or spend hours circling the airport. *The Cure for Jet Lag* will work, and work well, for everyone.

CHAPTER SIX

HOW TO CHOOSE THE RIGHT 3-STEP SYSTEM

Eastbound, Westbound and Complex Flight Plans

Planes fly east. Planes fly west. Some trips are nonstop and direct, while other flights zigzag, touching down several times along the way. You might be staying overnight at an interim stop and then flying out again the next day or several days later to yet another destination in a new time zone, eastbound or westbound.

Making or missing flight connections, biding your time during layovers, adjusting and readjusting flight itineraries as forces beyond your control result in canceled flights, delays or rerouting, make it important to have several customized 3-Step Systems on hand from which to choose in implementing *The Cure for Jet Lag*.

The 3-Step Systems are separated into three distinct chapters: Chapter Seven for eastbound flight plans in which you gain time (set your watch ahead), Chapter Eight for westbound flight plans in which you lose time (set your watch back), and Chapter Nine in which you may be setting your watch ahead several times during the trip, setting your watch back several times during the trip, or setting your watch ahead one day and back the next on more complicated flight plans.

During all the flights listed below, as you cross increasing numbers of time zones, the 3-Step System changes the timing of when and what you will eat, when you will drink black coffee or plain tea, when you will become physically and mentally active, and when you will sleep and wake up. That's why there are multiple plans from which to choose.

Chapter Seven: Eastbound Flights

Eastbound	1-2	Time Zones Crossed
Eastbound	3-4	Time Zones Crossed
Eastbound	5-6	Time Zones Crossed
Eastbound	7-8	Time Zones Crossed
Eastbound	9-10	Time Zones Crossed
Eastbound	11-12	Time Zones Crossed

Chapter Eight: Westbound Flights

Westbound	1-2	Time Zones Crossed
Westbound	3-4	Time Zones Crossed
Westbound	5-6	Time Zones Crossed
Westbound	7-8	Time Zones Crossed
Westbound	9-10	Time Zones Crossed
Westbound	11-12	Time Zones Crossed

Chapter Nine: Complex Flights.

Multi-Destination Flights, Same Direction—Short Stay

Multi-Destination Flights, Same Direction—Relatively Brief Stay

Multi-Destination Flights, East to West and West to East—Short Stay

Multi-Destination Flights, East to West and West to East—Varying Length of Stay

Multi-Destination Flights, Any Direction—Long Length of Stay

Timing Departure and Arrival Times

Avoid sleep deprivation. Sleep deprivation, no matter at which end of the day it occurs, begins to throw your body clocks off schedule and to precipitate the first stage of circadian dyschronism as your body clocks begin to go out of sync with one another. To the extent possible, pick a departure time that permits boarding the airplane during daylight hours, neither forcing you to rise early nor keeping you up too late.

If a limited selection of flight plans forces you to arrive too late in the day for the "active" phase of the 3-Step System, and if you expect to conduct business in an intelligent manner or enjoy yourself at your destination, then it would be a better plan to depart one day earlier in order to provide time for a good night's sleep.

Arrive During Daylight Hours. As important as it is to not be sleep-deprived on the first day of your trip, it is also crucial to design an itinerary and a flight plan that allow you to arrive at your destination during the "active" phase for local residents, which, as you follow *The Cure for Jet Lag*, will also be your active phase.

BEST DAY OF ARRIVAL

For Maximum Physical or Mental Performance After an Easterly Flight		
Time Zone Change	With Jet Lag Program	Without Jet Lag Program
+1	Same day arrival	Same day arrival
+2	Same day arrival	Same day arrival
+3	Same day arrival	Arrive one day early
+4	Same day arrival	Arrive two days early
+5	Arrive one day early	Arrive three to four days early
+6	Arrive one day early	Arrive four to six days early
+7	Arrive two days early	Arrive five to seven days early
+8	Arrive two days early	Arrive six to ten days early
+9	Arrive two days early	Arrive seven to eleven days early
+10	Arrive three days early	Arrive eight to twelve days early
+11	Arrive three days early	Arrive nine to twelve days early
+12	Arrive three days early	Arrive ten to twelve days early

For Maximum Physical or Mental Performance After a Westerly Flight		
Time Zone Change	With Jet Lag Program	Without Jet Lag Program
-1	Same day arrival	Same day arrival
-2	Same day arrival	Same day arrival
-3	Same day arrival	Arrive one day early
-4	Same day arrival	Arrive two days early
-5	Arrive one day early	Arrive three days early
-6	Arrive one day early	Arrive four days early
-7	Arrive one day early	Arrive five days early
-8	Arrive one day early	Arrive six days early
-9	Arrive two days early	Arrive seven days early
-10	Arrive two days early	Arrive eight to ten days early
-11	Arrive two or three days early	Arrive nine to eleven days early
-12	Arrive three days early	Arrive ten to twelve days early

If you arrive between midnight and dawn, destination time, then you will be forced to be very active immediately (disembarking, handling luggage, going through customs, taking ground transportation, checking in at a hotel, unpacking, etc.), at a time when you should be trying to sleep. All of this activity would be occurring at the very trough of the activity phase of the body clock cycle for local residents. Since the goal of the 3-Step System is to synchronize you to local time frames immediately upon arriving, a nighttime arrival interferes with the synchronization process.

If you must choose between an ideal departure time and an ideal arrival time, opt for the ideal arrival time.

Eastbound Flights

Eastbound Departure Times: For short trips east, don't lose too much sleep by getting up too early on the morning of the flight; for medium trips east, don't arrange a flight that forces you to awaken before 5:30 AM; and for long trips east, plan either:

- A fairly late departure (though before midnight) and an arrival the next morning (anytime after 6 AM, destination time, or

- A very early departure (though after 6 AM, home-time) and a very late arrival the same day (though before midnight, destination time).

Eastbound Arrival Times: Stated simply, the rule is to try to arrive sometime between 8 AM and 8 PM, with the earlier the better. Avoid arriving between midnight and 5 AM whenever possible.

Westbound Flights

Westbound Departure Times: For **short trips**, be sure to sleep at least as late as usual, and preferably later. For **medium trips west**, you may sleep as late as the expected new rising time at your destination, and pick a compatible flight. For **long trips west**, arrange your departure so as to assure the longest possible interval of rest during the fast phase that precedes the en route high-protein breakfast that will coincide with breakfast time at your destination. If you can sleep well on board a transoceanic plane, or if a sleeper is available, then departure should be as early as possible (but after 8 AM), to both reduce sleep deprivation during this very long day that accompanies flights west, and to provide for a prolonged interval of quiet and rest during the latter part of the fast that precedes destination time breakfast. Although a late departure before a long westbound trip allows you the luxury of a few additional hours of sleep early in the morning on the day of departure, thereby reducing the amount of sleep deprivation that you will accumulate, the late departure may deprive you of the rest you need during the late hours of your final fast period.

Westbound Arrival Times: Just like the eastbound trips, you want to arrive when everyone else at your destination is up and about, so that you take full advantage of the active phase of the 3-Step System. Try to arrive around breakfast time, if possible, or as early in the day as you can.

Four Questions to Ask Your Airline

You've selected your flight based on the ideal arrival and departure times, or as close to the ideal as you can book. Now find out the following information and write it down. (It's a lot smarter to have all the information about your flight written down so that you can integrate the 3-Step System smoothly, rather than "wing it" as you go.)

1. **How many time zones are you crossing and in which direction are you flying?** So many people still get confused about whether they are flying in an easterly direction or westerly direction. One more time: If you are setting your watch back to an earlier hour, you are flying west. If you are setting your watch forward to a later hour, you are flying east. Get it straight!

2. **How many hours are estimated for the entire flight?** While not a crucial question, it is valuable to know the total number of hours en route so that you can get a complete overview of your entire trip and know ahead of time when you are to drink black coffee or plain tea, sleep or exercise, and eat sparingly or indulge at breakfast destination time, even if you are still in the plane. Get organized!

3. **What time will meals be served and from what foods can you select?** On the off chance that meals are being served (these days, usually only in business class or first class), airlines may offer a variety of meal options. Given notice, they can often provide you with meals that are

vegetarian, kosher, low-sodium, low-cholesterol, or high-protein. And if no meals are served on the plane, prepare to bring your own so that you can stick with *The Cure for Jet Lag* 3-Step System when it calls for small meals or large meals, high carbohydrate or high protein. Be prepared!

4. **Can you pre-select your seat in the airplane?** You want to be physically removed from the area of the galley, lavatories, and bassinettes (where lots of distracting activities and noises may interrupt your "rest" periods). Try to arrange for plenty of leg room (near the emergency exits, in the front row of a section, and on the side of the plane opposite from where the sun will be when you are trying to sleep. Many airlines now charge extra for the most popular seats. Spend the money!

Transfer your flight information to *The Cure for Jet Lag* Itinerary Worksheets. As soon as you have your itinerary laid out, mark or set alerts in your personal calendar accordingly so that you know exactly when to start the preflight steps of feasting and fasting (eating lightly) if you have time before the day of the flight, and when to stop drinking caffeinated beverages.

Preflight, Inflight and Postflight Tip Sheet

Preflight

Pack the following items in a small bag to be carried onto the airplane: sleepshade, slipper socks, travel alarm, extra wristwatch (unless your normal wristwatch is of the type that can display two different time zones), toothbrush, toothpaste, gum, lip balm, nasal decongestant, and *The Cure for Jet Lag*.

1. Pack a clear plastic bag of leftovers from the refrigerator in case meals served on the airplane do not correspond to the high-protein breakfast and lunch and high-carbohydrate dinner system. Leftovers are also handy for light snacking in flight. Make sure your leftovers are stored in a clear plastic bag as required by airport security.

2. Wear loose clothing.

3. Do not let everything pile up until the last minute and get to the airport well in advance of the flight to reduce the chance of being bumped.

4. Try to avoid flying if you have a cold or ear problems. Remember that red wine, sherry, and port contain histamines that can aggravate head congestion.

5. Check the weather at your destination and plan accordingly.

6. Make sure you use your small portable luggage cart, or luggage on wheels as a "back saving" device.

Inflight

7. Drink lots of fluids. The atmosphere in the airplane's cabin is as dry as the Gobi Desert.

8. If there are any empty seats on the airplane and you are allowed to do so, make a quick move to a row of seats that can be converted into a quasi-bed for the "inactive" phase of *The Cure for Jet Lag*.

9. Bring a pillow and blanket for the "inactive" phase of *The Cure for Jet Lag*. Covering yourself with a blanket helps keep you comfortable as your body temperature drops during inactivity. A pillow is a familiar psychological device that enhances your ability to sleep.

10. Loosen your clothing as an aid to circulation. Take off your shoes.

11. Avoid alcohol or limit it. Alcohol tends to add to the dehydration problem of poor cabin pressurization that pushes the humidity to as low as 5% or even 2%.

12. If you wear contact lenses, consider removing them while in flight so that your eyes do not become irritated because of the extremely dry atmosphere in the cabin.

Postflight

13. Upon arrival, in your excitement at having landed at your destination, do not disregard the Postflight Steps of *The Cure for Jet Lag*.

14. Remember to plan ahead for your next or return flight and implement the Preflight Steps of the System in plenty of time to assure the maximum benefits.

Now you are ready to begin the specific instructions for your eastbound, westbound, or complex flights.

CHAPTER SEVEN

EASTBOUND FLIGHTS

EASTBOUND PHASE ADVANCE 1-2 TIME ZONES

degrees longitude E & W

From	To	# Zones	ml/km	Flight Time (h)
Pago Pago [1]	Honolulu [2]	1	2612/4204	4.5
Papeete [2]	Los Angeles [4]	2	4109/6613	7.1
Vancouver [4]	Mexico City [6]	2	2452/3946	4.3
Denver [5]	Washington [7]	2	1464/2356	2.5
New Orleans [6]	San Juan [8]	2	1713/2757	3.0

of Greenwich Meridian ⤴

From	To	# Zones	ml/km	Flight Time (h)
Buenos Aires [9]	Santa Maria (AZ) [11]	2	6031/9707	10.4
Accra [12]	Frankfurt [13]	1	3110/5006	5.4
Rome [13]	Nairobi [15]	2	3353/5396	5.8
Manila [20]	Sydney [22]	2	3888/6258	6.7
Melbourne [22]	Wellington [24]	2	1545/2566	4.5

Eastbound 1-2 Time Zones

Although a one-hour to two-hour time zone change does not cause as much body clock upheaval as trips of a greater distance, even such a minimal change can produce jet lag symptoms that cause mild fatigue, poor appetite, gastrointestinal difficulties, and some confusion for at least a few days. To avoid jet lag symptoms completely, follow the simple steps outlined below. Also, don't forget to refer to the Suggested Menus and Composition of Foods/Calorie Counter table in Chapter Twelve and the list of Major Influences on Body Clocks in Chapter Four.

FEAST = Generous servings FAST = Limited portions	
STEP #1	
TWO days before the flight	• Stop consuming beverages, food, or drugs containing methylated xanthines (coffee, tea, cocoa, chocolate, diet aids, etc.) in the early morning or late at night. • Feel free, however, to drink caffeinated beverages between 3 PM and 4:30 PM.
ONE day before the flight	• Eat a low-calorie HIGH-PROTEIN breakfast and a low-calorie HIGH-PROTEIN lunch. • Follow with a low-calorie HIGH-CARBOHYDRATE dinner. • Because this is a FAST day, keep the meals low in calories: a daily total of 800 is ideal.
Night before the flight	• Shortly after 6 PM, DRINK TWO TO THREE CUPS of black coffee or strong, plain tea. • Prior to going to bed set your alarm clock to wake up one hour before breakfast time at your destination.

STEP #2	
Morning of the flight	• Get out of bed earlier than usual. • SET A WATCH TO DESTINATION TIME. • A half-hour before breakfast, destination time, activate your body and mind (see Chapter Eleven, Mental and Physical Exercise Program). • Begin STEP THREE with breakfast, destination time.

STEP #3	
Breakfast destination time	• This is a FEAST day, so make it a hearty HIGH-PROTEIN breakfast on destination time and a hearty HIGH-PROTEIN lunch.
	• Follow with a hearty HIGH-CARBOHYDRATE dinner.
	• Drink water all day to compensate for the dehydration that is common on flights.
	• Limit alcoholic beverages to no more than one drink (better yet, don't drink at all).
	• Do not have any caffeinated beverages, foods, or drugs at all this entire day.
	• Since midnight destination time is 10 PM "old time," rest or sleep as soon as possible on destination time even if you do not feel tired. Wear a sleep mask, if necessary.
	Optional: For optimum energy, consider continuing the regimen of high-protein breakfasts and lunches, and high-carbohydrate dinners for the duration of your trip—until it is time to begin *The Cure for Jet Lag's* return-flight instructions. Also, keep in mind that your body clock is now set for destination time. From now on, if you drink caffeinated coffee or tea (except between 3 PM and 4:30 PM), you WILL feel the effects of sleepiness in the morning and sleeplessness at night.

EASTBOUND PHASE ADVANCE 3-4 TIME ZONES

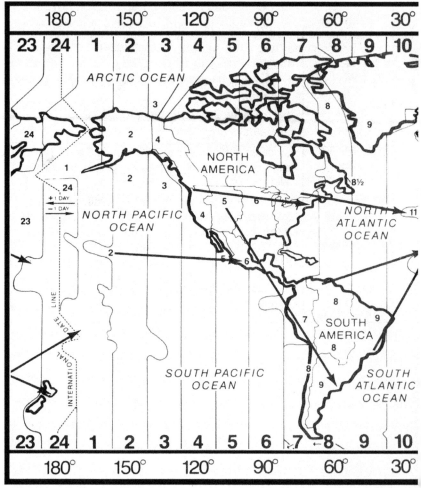

↖ degrees longitude E & W

From	To	# Zones	ml/km	Flight Time (h)
Honolulu [2]	Mexico City [6]	4	3781/6084	6.6
Seattle [4]	Boston [7]	3	2496/4016	4.3
Denver [5]	Buenos Aires [9]	4	5928/9538	10.3
Montreal [7]	Santa Maria (AZ) [11]	4	2552/4106	4.4
Caracas [8]	Las Palmas [12]	4	3540/5696	6.1

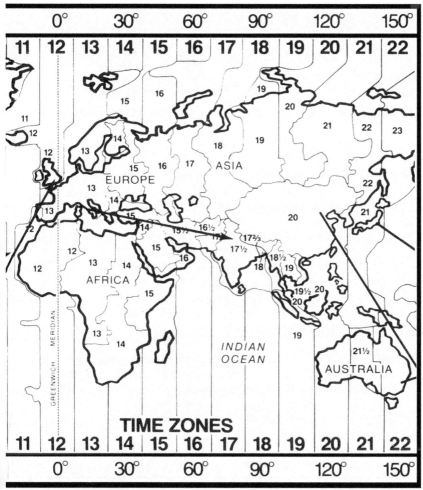

of Greenwich Meridian ➚

From	To	# Zones	ml/km	Flight Time (h)
Rio de Janeiro [9]	London [12]	3	5746/9248	9.9
Rome [13]	Delhi [17.5]	4.5	3685/5929	6.4
Beijing [20]	Wellington [24]	4	6698/10777	11.6
Tokyo [21]	Wake [24]	3	1983/3192	3.4
Sydney [22]	Pago Pago [1]	3	2733/4399	4.7

Eastbound 3-4 Time Zones

The three-hour to four-hour time zone change represents a significant jolt to your biochemical systems. Even though you may consider a coast-to-coast United States flight or a continent-to-continent flight from Rio de Janeiro to London a minor trip, major jet lag symptoms are in store for you without *The Cure for Jet Lag*. Implementing the 3-Step System for three-hour to four-hour shifts will greatly reduce the symptoms you experience. Since jet lag symptoms abate at different times and at different rates, by following the steps outlined below you will find that those symptoms that would have lingered a day or two may well not occur and those symptoms that might have taken days or weeks to subside will end quite rapidly. Also, don't forget to refer to the Suggested Menus and Composition of Foods/Calorie Counter table in Chapter Twelve and the list of Major Influences on Body Clocks in Chapter Four.

FEAST = Generous servings FAST = Limited portions	
STEP #1	
THREE days before the flight	• Stop consuming beverages, food, or drugs containing methylated xanthines (coffee, tea, cocoa, chocolate, diet aids, etc.) in the early morning or late at night. • Feel free, however, to drink caffeinated beverages between 3 PM and 4:30 PM.
ONE day before the flight	• This is a FEAST day, so make it a hearty HIGH-PROTEIN breakfast and a hearty HIGH-PROTEIN lunch. • Follow with a hearty HIGH-CARBOHYDRATE dinner.

STEP #2	
Day of the flight	• Get out of bed earlier than usual. • Eat a low-calorie HIGH-PROTEIN breakfast and a low-calorie HIGH-PROTEIN lunch. • Follow with a low-calorie HIGH-CARBOHYDRATE dinner. • Because this is a FAST day, keep the meals low in calories; a daily total of 800 calories is ideal. • Drink water all day to compensate for the dehydration that is common on flights.

STEP #2 continued	
Day of the flight	• Limit alcoholic beverages to no more than one drink (better yet, don't drink at all). • Shortly after 6 PM, no matter where you are or what you are doing, whether you are still in the airplane or not, DRINK TWO TO THREE CUPS of black coffee or strong, plain tea. • RESET YOUR WATCH TO DESTINATION TIME. • Since midnight destination time is 8 PM "old time," try to rest or sleep as soon as possible—on destination time—even if you do not feel tired—until morning, destination time. Wear a sleep mask if necessary. • Set your alarm to wake up one hour before breakfast, destination time.

STEP #3	
Day after the flight	• Do NOT oversleep. • A half-hour before breakfast, destination time, activate your body and brain (see Chapter Eleven, Mental and Physical Exercise Program). • This is a FEAST day, so when you get up, eat a hearty HIGH-PROTEIN breakfast on destination time and a hearty HIGH-PROTEIN lunch. • Follow with a hearty HIGH-CARBOHYDRATE dinner. • Do NOT have any caffeinated beverages, foods, or drugs at all today. • Keep active. Do NOT nap. • Get to bed by 10:30 PM, destination time. • (You may prefer to consider this day to be the flight day; if so, simply shift each step of the above to one day earlier.) *Optional*: For optimum energy, consider continuing the regimen of high-protein breakfasts and lunches, and high-carbohydrate dinners for the duration of your trip—until it is time to begin *The Cure for Jet Lag's* return-flight instructions. Also, keep in mind that your body clock is now set for destination time. From now on, if you drink caffeinated coffee or tea (except between 3 PM and 4:30 PM), you WILL feel the effects of sleepiness in the morning and sleeplessness at night.

EASTBOUND PHASE ADVANCE 5 or 6 TIME ZONES

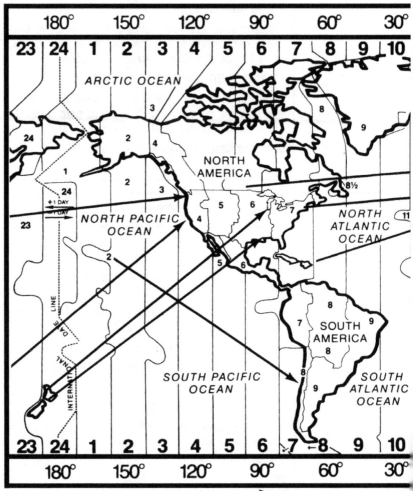

degrees longitude E & W

From	To	# Zones	ml/km	Flight Time (h)
Honolulu [2]	Valparaiso [8]	6	6793/10930	11.7
Winnipeg [6]	Glasgow [12]	6	3599/5791	6.2
Boston [7]	Frankfurt [13]	6	3660/5889	6.3
San Juan [8]	Madrid [13]	5	3966/6382	6.9
Santa Maria (AZ) [11]	Calcutta [17.5]	6.5	6549/10538	11.3

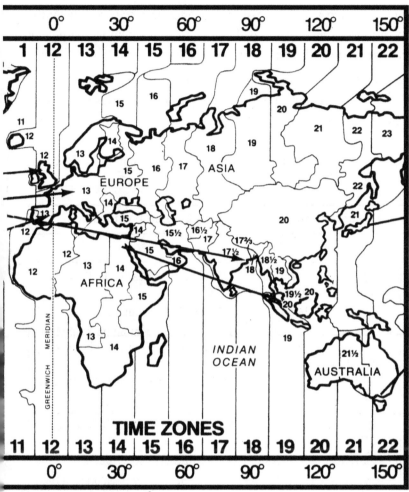

of Greenwich Meridian ↗

From	To	# Zones	ml/km	Flight Time (h)
Cairo [14]	Singapore [20]	6	5088/8187	8.8
Tokyo [21]	Seattle [4]	6	4790/7708	8.3
Melbourne [22]	San Francisco [4]	6	7854/12637	13.6
Wellington [24]	New Orleans [6]	6	7794/12541	13.5
Auckland [24]	Chicago [6]	6	8309/13369	14.4

Eastbound 5-6 Time Zones

Anyone who has experienced the jet lag symptoms associated with a five-hour to six-hour time zone change knows that he or she can become quite overwhelmed. For this reason, travelers crossing five-to-six time zones or more are usually the first to complain seriously about anticipated debilitation. They know that jet lag will be a significant problem with which they must reckon.

Again, you are bound to have symptoms, but with *The Cure for Jet Lag,* they will be greatly minimized. You should find that sleep, in particular, arrives more easily with the 3-Step System than without it. Follow the simple steps outlined below. Also, don't forget to refer to the Suggested Menus and Composition of Foods/Calorie Counter table in Chapter Twelve and the list of Major Influences on Body Clocks in Chapter Four.

FEAST = Generous servings FAST = Limited portions	
STEP #1	
THREE days before the flight	• Begin the System with a FEAST day of a hearty HIGH-PROTEIN breakfast and a hearty HIGH-PROTEIN lunch. • Follow with a hearty HIGH-CARBOHYDRATE dinner. • Stop consuming beverages, food, or drugs containing methylated xanthines (coffee, tea, cocoa, chocolate, diet aids, etc.) in the early morning or late at night. • Feel free, however, to drink caffeinated beverages between 3 PM and 4:30 PM.
TWO days before the flight	• Eat a low-calorie HIGH-PROTEIN breakfast and a low-calorie HIGH-PROTEIN lunch. • Follow with a low-calorie HIGH-CARBOHYDRATE dinner. • Because this is a FAST day, keep the meals low in calories; a daily total of 800 calories is ideal. • Do NOT eat any snacks after dinner.
ONE day before the flight	• This is a FEAST day, so start the day with a hearty HIGH-PROTEIN breakfast and a hearty HIGH-PROTEIN lunch. • Follow with a hearty HIGH-CARBOHYDRATE dinner. • Do NOT eat any snacks after dinner.

	STEP #2
Day of the flight	• Get out of bed earlier than usual.
	• Eat a low-calorie HIGH-PROTEIN breakfast and low-calorie HIGH-PROTEIN lunch.
	• Follow with a low-calorie HIGH-CARBOHYDRATE dinner.
	• Because this is a FAST day, keep the meals low in calories; a daily total of 800 calories is ideal.
	• Drink water all day to compensate for the dehydration that is common on flights.
	• Limit alcoholic beverages to no more than one drink (better yet, don't drink at all).
	• Shortly after 6 PM, no matter where you are or what you are doing, whether you are still in the airplane or not, DRINK TWO TO THREE CUPS of black coffee or strong, plain tea.
	• RESET YOUR WR1STWATCH TO DESTINATION TIME.
	• Since midnight destination time is 6 PM "old time," try to rest or sleep as soon as possible on destination time—even if you do not feel tired— until morning, destination time. Wear a sleep mask if necessary.

	STEP #3
Breakfast destination time	• Do NOT oversleep.
	• A half-hour before breakfast, destination time, activate your body and brain (see Chapter Twelve, Mental and Physical Exercise Program).
	• This is a FEAST day, so when you eat, have a hearty HIGH-PROTEIN breakfast on destination time (remember: this meal usually occurs in flight) and a hearty, HIGH-PROTEIN lunch.
	• Follow with a hearty HIGH-CARBOHYDRATE dinner.
	• Do NOT snack after dinner.
	• Do NOT have any caffeinated beverages, foods, or drugs at all today.
	• Keep active. Do NOT nap.
	• Get to bed early, by 10 PM, destination time.
	Optional: For optimum energy, consider continuing the regimen of high-protein breakfasts and lunches, and high-carbohydrate dinners for the duration of your trip—until it is time to begin *The Cure for Jet Lag's* return-flight instructions. Also, keep in mind that your body clock is now set for destination time. From now on, if you drink caffeinated coffee or tea (except between 3 PM and 4:30 PM), you WILL feel the effects of sleepiness in the morning and sleeplessness at night.

EASTBOUND PHASE ADVANCE 7 or 8 TIME ZONES

↰ degrees longitude E & W

From	To	# Zones	ml/km	Flight Time (h)
Nome [1]	Valparaiso [8]	7	8360/13451	14.4
Edmonton [5]	Amsterdam [13]	8	4323/6955	7.5
New York [7]	Tel Aviv [14]	7	5672/9126	9.8
Valparaiso [8]	Moscow [15]	7	8792/14146	15.2
Rio de Janeiro [9]	Bombay [17.5]	8.5	8257/13286	14.3

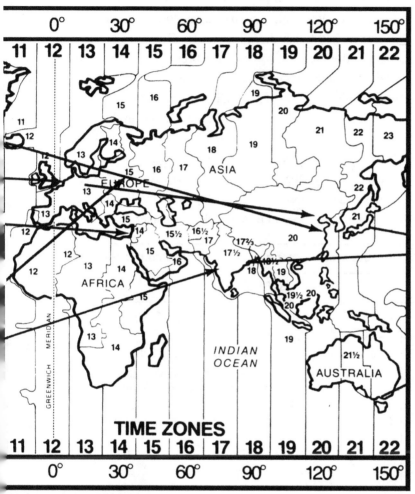

of Greenwich Meridian ⤴

From	To	# Zones	ml/km	Flight Time (h)
Reykjavik [12]	Shanghai [20]	8	5559/8945	9.6
Berlin [13]	Beijing [20]	7	4567/7348	7.9
Calcutta [17.5]	Honolulu [2]	8.5	5271/8481	9.1
Tokyo [21]	Los Angeles [4]	7	5470/8802	9.5
Melbourne [22]	Mexico City [6]	8	8422/13551	14.6

Eastbound 7-8 Time Zones

A seven-hour or eight-hour time zone change causes severe jet lag symptoms that can virtually incapacitate you, mentally and physically, for days if not for weeks. On an easterly flight involving such a significant time change, you lose a large portion of sleep. For example, if you take an 8 PM flight from Edmonton, Canada to Amsterdam, you may be in the middle of a deep sleep (if you have not been up all those hours because of the excitement of the trip or the noise of the airplane) when it is time to land. When you land after a severely limited amount of sleep, it is time to function optimally to pass through customs, and time to get to your hotel or motel. Getting up in the middle of the night and functioning coherently is not easy, but this is precisely what is called for in long-distance, multi-meridional flights. By following the simple steps outlined below, you should be able to step right into the mainstream of activity. Also, don't forget to refer to the Suggested Menus and Composition of Foods/Calorie Counter table in Chapter Twelve and the list of Major Influences on Body Clocks in Chapter Four.

FEAST = Generous servings FAST = Limited portions	
STEP #1	
THREE days before the flight	• This is a FEAST day, so eat a hearty HIGH-PROTEIN breakfast and a hearty HIGH-PROTEIN lunch. • Follow with a hearty HIGH-CARBOHYDRATE dinner. • STOP consuming beverages, foods, or drugs containing methylated xanthines (coffee, tea, cocoa, or chocolate, etc.) in the early morning or late at night. • Feel free, however, to drink caffeinated beverages between 3 PM and 4:30 PM.
TWO days before the flight	• Eat a low-calorie HIGH-PROTEIN breakfast and a low-calorie HIGH-PROTEIN lunch. • Follow with a low-calorie HIGH-CARBOHYDRATE dinner. • Because this is a FAST day, keep the meals low in calories; a daily total of 800 calories is ideal. • Do NOT eat any snacks after dinner.
ONE day before the flight	• This is a FEAST day, so eat a hearty HIGH-PROTEIN breakfast and a hearty HIGH-PROTEIN lunch. • Follow with a hearty HIGH-CARBOHYDRATE dinner. • Do NOT eat any snacks after dinner.

STEP #2	
Morning of the flight	• Get out of bed earlier than usual. • Eat a low-calorie HIGH-PROTEIN breakfast and a low-calorie HIGH-PROTEIN lunch. • Follow with a low-calorie HIGH-CARBOHYDRATE dinner (you may want to skip this meal as breakfast destination time comes so soon). • Because this is a FAST day, keep the meals low in calories; a daily total of 800 calories is ideal. • Drink water all day to compensate for the dehydration that is common on flights. Limit alcoholic beverages to no more than one drink (better yet, don't drink at all). • Shortly after 6 PM, no matter where you are or what you are doing, whether you are still in the airplane or not, DRINK ONE TO TWO CUPS of black coffee or strong, plain tea. • RESET YOUR WRISTWATCH TO DESTINATION TIME. • Since midnight destination time is 4 PM "old time," try to rest or sleep as soon as possible on destination time—even if you don't feel tired—until morning time. Wear a sleep mask if necessary.

STEP #3	
Breakfast destination time	• Do NOT oversleep. • A half-hour before breakfast, destination time, activate your body and brain. (See Chapter Eleven, Mental and Physical Exercise.) • DRINK ONE TO TWO CUPS of black coffee or strong, plain tea between 6 AM and 7:30 AM, destination time, at destination time breakfast. • Do NOT have any methylated xanthines at all today after breakfast. • Keep active all day. Do NOT nap. • This is a FEAST day, so when you eat have a hearty HIGH-PROTEIN breakfast on destination time and a hearty HIGH-PROTEIN lunch • Follow with a hearty HIGH-CARBOHYDRATE dinner. • Do NOT snack after dinner. • Get to bed by 10 PM, destination time. *Optional*: For optimum energy, consider continuing the regimen of high-protein breakfasts and lunches, and high-carbohydrate dinners for the duration of your trip—until it is time to begin *The Cure for Jet Lag's* return-flight instructions. Also, keep in mind that your body clock is now set for destination time. From now on, if you drink caffeinated coffee or tea (except between 3 PM and 4:30 PM), you WILL feel the effects of sleepiness in the morning and sleeplessness at night.

EASTBOUND PHASE ADVANCE 9 OR 10 TIME ZONES

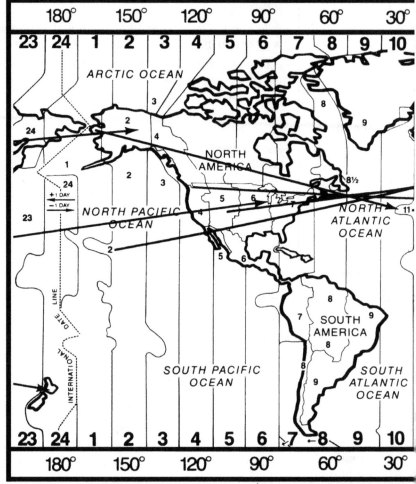

↖ degrees longitude E & W

From	To	# Zones	ml/km	Flight Time (h)
Nome [1]	Santa Maria (AZ) [11]	10	4954/7971	8.6
Honolulu [2]	London [12]	10	7226/11627	12.5
Seattle [4]	Istanbul [14]	10	6061/9752	10.5
Denver [5]	Moscow [15]	10	5785/8826	9.5
Boston [7]	Sverdlovsk [17]	10	5025/8085	8.7

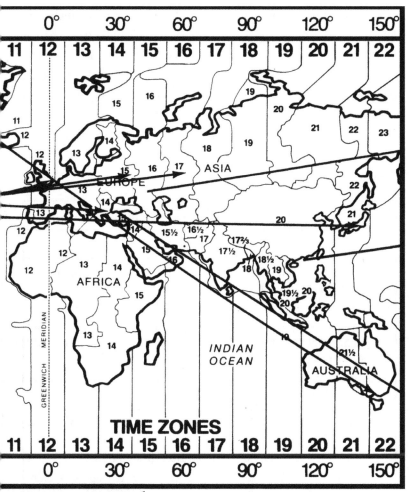

of Greenwich Meridian ⤴

From	To	# Zones	ml/km	Flight Time (h)
Santa Maria (AZ) [11]	Tokyo [21]	10	7247/11661	12.5
Reykjavik [12]	Melbourne [22]	10	10544/16966	18.2
Istanbul [14]	Wellington [24]	10	10663/17157	18.4
Volgograd [16]	Fairbanks [2]	10	4560/7337	7.9
Hong Kong [20]	Chicago [6]	10	7790/12534	13.5

Eastbound 9-10 Time Zones

The most significant problem associated with a huge time zone change such as a nine-hour to ten-hour time zone advance is the shattering of sleeping and waking schedules. A nine-hour to ten-hour advance in time constitutes a switch from night into day or day into night. You are losing an entire night's sleep, and this holds true whether you are on *The Cure for Jet Lag* or not. 10 PM is 8 AM destination time! The problem, therefore, is how to handle not only the circadian phase change, but also the sleep deprivation so that you can assume destination time activities right away. The key, of course, is to take advantage of *The Cure for Jet Lag*. Follow the simple steps outlined below. Also, don't forget to refer to the Suggested Menus and Composition of Foods/Calorie Counter table in Chapter Twelve and the list of Major Influences on Body Clocks in Chapter Four.

FEAST = Generous servings FAST = Limited portions	
STEP #1	
THREE days before the flight	• This is a FEAST day, so begin the System by eating a hearty HIGH-PROTEIN breakfast and a high-calorie HIGH-PROTEIN lunch. • Follow with a hearty HIGH-CARBOHYDRATE dinner. • STOP consuming beverages, foods, or drugs containing methylated xanthines (coffee, tea, cocoa, or chocolate, etc.) in the early morning or late at night. • Feel free, however, to drink caffeinated beverages between 3 PM and 4:30 PM.
TWO days before the flight	• Eat a low-calorie HIGH-PROTEIN breakfast and a low-calorie HIGH-PROTEIN lunch. • Follow with a low-calorie HIGH-CARBOHYDRATE dinner. • Because this is a FAST day, keep the meals low in calories; a daily total of 800 calories is ideal. • Do NOT eat any snacks after dinner.
ONE day before the flight	• The day before the flight is a FEAST day, so eat a hearty HIGH-PROTEIN breakfast and a hearty HIGH-PROTEIN lunch. • Follow with a hearty HIGH-CARBOHYDRATE dinner. • Do NOT eat any snacks after dinner. • Go to bed earlier than usual.

STEP #2

Morning of the flight	• Get out of bed earlier than usual.
	• Eat a low-calorie HIGH-PROTEIN breakfast and also a low-calorie HIGH-PROTEIN lunch. Because this is a FAST day, keep the meals low in calories.
	• You are only eating two meals, and they should be very light; therefore, a daily total of 400 calories is ideal.
	• RIGHT AFTER LUNCH MAKE SURE TO RESET YOUR WRISTWATCH TO DESTINATION TIME.
	• Do not eat another meal until breakfast, destination time.
	• Drink water all day to compensate for the dehydration that is common on flights.
	• Limit alcoholic beverages to no more than one drink (better yet, don't drink at all).
	• Since midnight destination time is 2 PM "old time," try to rest or sleep as soon as possible on destination time—even if you don't feel tired—until morning destination time. Wear a sleep mask if necessary.

STEP #3

Breakfast destination time	• A half-hour before breakfast, destination time, activate your body and brain (See Chapter Eleven, Mental and Physical Exercise Program).
	• Before breakfast (and no later than 9:30 AM), DRINK TWO TO THREE CUPS of black coffee or strong, plain tea.
	• This is a FEAST day, so when you eat, have a hearty HIGH-PROTEIN breakfast on destination time and a hearty HIGH-PROTEIN lunch.
	• Follow with a hearty HIGH-CARBOHYDRATE dinner.
	• Keep Active. Do NOT nap. Get to bed early.
	Optional: For optimum energy, consider continuing the regimen of high-protein breakfasts and lunches, and high-carbohydrate dinners for the duration of your trip—until it is time to begin *The Cure for Jet Lag's* return-flight instructions. Also, keep in mind that your body clock is now set for destination time. From now on, if you drink caffeinated coffee or tea (except between 3 PM and 4:30 PM), you WILL feel the effects of sleepiness in the morning and sleeplessness at night.

EASTBOUND PHASE ADVANCE 11 or 12 TIME ZONES

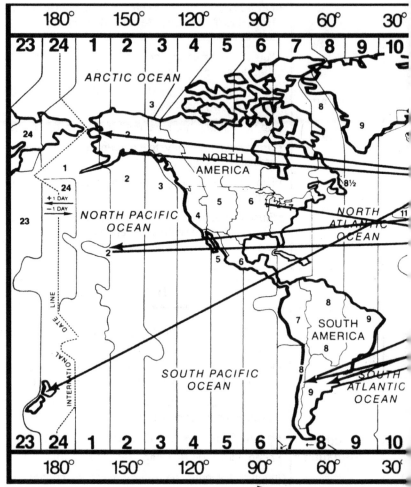

degrees longitude E & W

From	To	# Zones	ml/km	Flight Time (h)
Honolulu [2]	Cairo [14]	12	8738/14060	15.1
Anchorage [2]	Amsterdam [13]	11	4475/7201	7.8
Chicago [6]	Calcutta [17.5]	11.5	7981/12842	13.8
Valparaiso [8]	Beijing [20]	12	8088/13014	14.0
Buenos Aires [9]	Singapore [20]	11	9864/15871	17.0

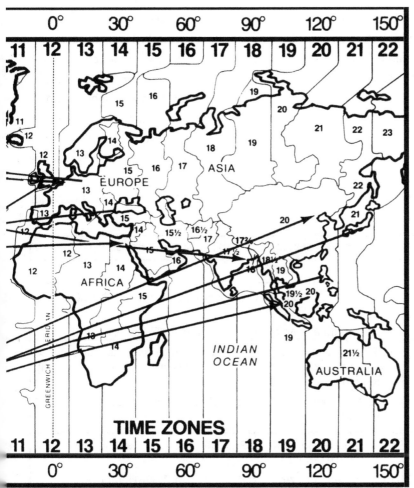

of Greenwich Meridian ↗

From	To	# Zones	ml/km	Flight Time (h)
London [12]	Wellington [24]	12	11682/18797	20.2
Berlin [13]	Nome [1]	12	4342/6987	7.5
Istanbul [14]	Honolulu [2]	12	8104/13040	14.0
Manila [20]	Valparaiso [8]	12	10930/17587	18.9
Tokyo [21]	Buenos Aires [9]	12	11400/18343	19.7

Eastbound 11-12 Time Zones

In either direction, east or west, the eleven-hour to twelve-hour time zone change represents the most grueling body clock upheaval in transmeridional travel. Wherever your airplane lands in the world, when there has been an eleven- or twelve-hour time change, your body clocks must complete a 180-degree phase shift. Although your body is programmed naturally to be asleep, it must now remain alert. When your body clocks normally see that you are bright-eyed and energetic, sleep must be induced. All the mental and physical skills that peak and trough during the daytime and nighttime hours must now make a total shift to a schedule that is not only new, but the complete opposite of the old schedule. Left to their own devices, body clocks can require literally weeks to reorganize and resynchronize. Not, however, with *The Cure for Jet Lag*. Follow the simple steps outlined below. Also, don't forget to refer to the Suggested Menus and Composition of Foods/Calorie Counter table in Chapter Twelve and the list of Major Influences on Body Clocks in Chapter Four.

FEAST = Generous servings FAST = Limited portions	
STEP #1	
THREE days before the flight	• This is a FEAST day, so eat a hearty HIGH-PROTEIN breakfast and a hearty HIGH-PROTEIN lunch. • Follow with a hearty HIGH-CARBOHYDRATE dinner. • STOP consuming beverages, foods, or drugs containing methylated xanthines (coffee, tea, cocoa, or chocolate, etc.) in the early morning or late at night. • Feel free, however, to consume caffeinated beverages between 3 PM and 4:30 PM.
TWO days before the flight	• Eat a low-calorie HIGH-PROTEIN breakfast and a low-calorie HIGH-PROTEIN lunch. • Follow with a low-calorie HIGH-CARBOHYDRATE dinner. • Because this is a FAST day, keep the meals low in calories; a daily total of 800 calories is ideal. • Do NOT eat any snacks after dinner.
ONE day before the flight	• This is a FEAST day, so eat a hearty HIGH-PROTEIN breakfast and a hearty HIGH-PROTEIN lunch. • Follow with a hearty HIGH-CARBOHYDRATE dinner. • Do NOT eat any snacks after dinner. • Drink caffeinated beverages only between 7 AM and 11:30 AM this day.

STEP #2	
Morning of the flight	• Just before breakfast, and between 7 AM and 11:30 AM, DRINK TWO TO THREE CUPS of black coffee or strong, plain tea. • Eat a low-calorie HIGH-PROTEIN breakfast and a low-calorie HIGH-PROTEIN lunch (or skip lunch). You are only eating one or two meals in this FAST phase; a daily total of 400 calories is ideal. • RESET YOUR WRISTWATCH TO DESTINATION TIME. • Do NOT eat again until destination time breakfast. • Drink water all day to compensate for the dehydration that is common on flights. Limit alcoholic beverages to no more than one drink (better yet, don't drink at all). • Since midnight destination time is noon "old time," try to rest or sleep as soon as possible—even if you do not feel tired—until morning destination time. Wear an eye mask if necessary.

STEP #3	
Breakfast destination time	• A half-hour before breakfast, destination time, activate your body and brain. (See Chapter Eleven, Mental and Physical Exercise Program.) • This is a FEAST day, so eat a hearty HIGH-PROTEIN breakfast on destination time and a hearty HIGH-PROTEIN lunch. • Follow with a hearty HIGH-CARBOHYDRATE dinner. • Do NOT consume any methylated xanthines at all today. • Keep active. Do NOT nap. • Get to bed by 10 PM, destination time. *Optional*: For optimum energy, consider continuing the regimen of high-protein breakfasts and lunches, and high-carbohydrate dinners for the duration of your trip—until it is time to begin *The Cure for Jet Lag's* return-flight instructions. Also, keep in mind that your body clock is now set for destination time. From now on, if you drink caffeinated coffee or tea (except between 3 PM and 4:30 PM), you WILL feel the effects of sleepiness in the morning and sleeplessness at night.

CHAPTER EIGHT
WESTBOUND FLIGHTS

WESTBOUND PHASE DELAY 1 or 2 TIME ZONES

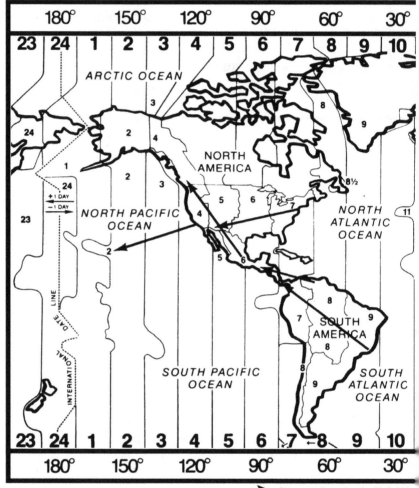

↖ degrees longitude E & W

From	To	# Zones	ml/km	Flight Time (h)
Los Angeles [4]	Honolulu [2]	2	2551/4106	4.4
Mexico City [6]	Vancouver [4]	2	2448/3940	4.3
New York [7]	Phoenix [5]	2	2029/3265	3.5
Rio de Janeiro [9]	Panama [7]	2	3289/5293	5.7
Caracas [8]	Guatemala [6]	2	1609/2590	2.8

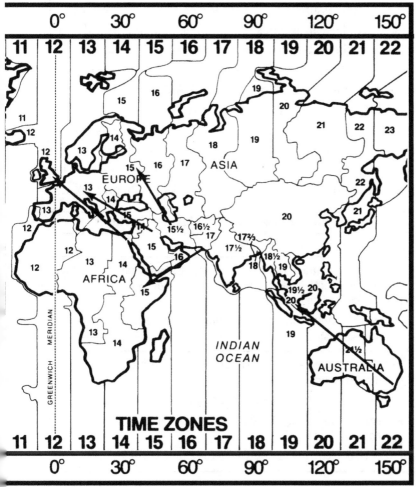

of Greenwich Meridian ⤴

From	To	# Zones	ml/km	Flight Time (h)
Baghdad [15]	Munich [13]	2	1970/3170	5.5
Cairo [14]	London [12]	2	2192/3528	3.8
Teheran [15.5]	Moscow [15]	.5	1545/2486	2.7
Karachi [17]	Addis Ababa [15]	2	2167/3486	3.4
Sydney [22]	Singapore [20]	2	3912/6296	6.8

Westbound 1-2 Time Zones

For reasons that are not yet clearly understood by scientists and researchers, recovery periods after a westbound journey take significantly less time than recovery periods after an eastbound trip. The assumption is that for whatever reason, you can adjust more readily to a schedule that expands the number of hours in a day than a schedule that condenses them. Perhaps that's because when you fly in a westerly direction, you have the luxury of additional time to catch up on sleep. For example, if after flying from Boston to Chicago you awake at 7 AM local time, it is actually 8 AM back in Boston, and you've slept for an extra hour. Nonetheless, even a single time zone change can produce symptoms you might wish to avoid. Follow the simple steps outlined below. Also, don't forget to refer to the Suggested Menus and Composition of Foods/Calorie Counter table in Chapter Twelve and the list of Major Influences on Body Clocks in Chapter Four.

FEAST = Generous servings FAST = Limited portions	
STEP #1	
TWO days before the flight	• Stop consuming beverages, food, or drugs containing methylated xanthines (coffee, tea, cocoa, chocolate, diet aids, etc.) in the early morning or late at night. • Feel free, however, to drink caffeinated beverages between 3 PM and 4:30 PM.
ONE day before the flight	• Eat a low-calorie HIGH-PROTEIN breakfast and a low-calorie HIGH-PROTEIN lunch. • Follow with a low-calorie HIGH-CARBOHYDRATE dinner. • Because this is a FAST day, keep the meals low in calories: a daily total of 800 is ideal. • Consume coffee or tea between 7 AM and 11 AM *only*.

STEP #2	
Morning of the flight	• Immediately upon rising (but no later than 11 AM) on the day of the flight drink TWO TO THREE CUPS of black coffee or strong, plain tea. • Do NOT consume any more methylated xanthines today. • SET WATCH TO DESTINATION TIME. • Begin STEP THREE at breakfast, destination time.

STEP #3

Breakfast destination time	• A half-hour before breakfast, destination time, activate your body and mind (see Chapter Eleven, Mental and Physical Exercise Program).
	• This is a FEAST day, so make it a hearty HIGH-PROTEIN breakfast on destination time and a hearty HIGH-PROTEIN lunch.
	• Follow with a hearty HIGH-CARBOHYDRATE dinner.
	• Light snacks after dinner are permissible.
	• Drink water all day to compensate for the dehydration that is common on flights.
	• Limit alcoholic beverages to no more than one drink (better yet, don't drink at all).
	• Do not consume any caffeinated beverages, foods, or drugs at all this entire day.
	• Since 10 PM destination time is midnight "old time," try to rest or sleep as soon as possible on destination time. Wear a sleep mask if necessary.
	Optional: For optimum energy, consider continuing the regimen of high-protein breakfasts and lunches, and high-carbohydrate dinners for the duration of your trip—until it is time to begin *The Cure for Jet Lag's* return-flight instructions. Also, keep in mind that your body clock is now set for destination time. From now on, if you drink caffeinated coffee or tea (except between 3 PM and 4:30 PM), you WILL feel the effects of sleepiness in the morning and sleeplessness at night.

WESTBOUND PHASE DELAY 3 or 4 TIME ZONES

↖ degrees longitude E & W

From	To	# Zones	ml/km	Flight Time (h)
Fairbanks [2]	Vladivostok [22]	4	3305/5318	5.7
Juneau [4]	Wellington [24]	4	7475/12028	12.9
New Orleans [6]	Honolulu [2]	4	4207/6769	7.3
Atlanta [7]	San Francisco [4]	3	2139/3442	3.7
Valparaiso [8]	Seattle [4]	4	6230/10024	10.8

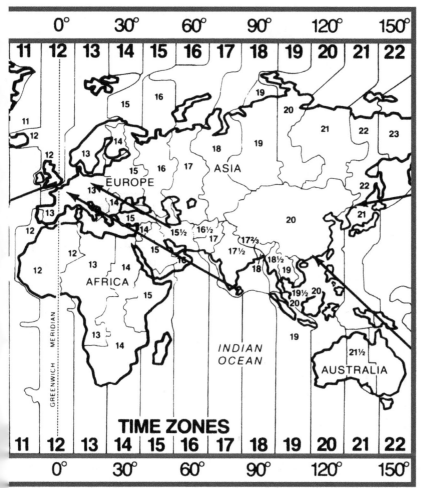

of Greenwich Meridian ↗

From	To	# Zones	ml/km	Flight Time (h)
Santa Maria (AZ) [11]	Boston [7]	4	2436/3920	4.2
London [12]	Bermuda [8]	4	3428/5514	5.9
Teheran [15.5]	Munich [13]	2.5	2179/3507	3.8
Colombo [17.5]	Paris [13]	4.5	5292/8516	9.2
Wellington [24]	Hong Kong [20]	4	5853/9418	10.1

Westbound 3-4 Time Zones

Even though a three-hour to four-hour time zone change may still sound relatively insignificant, the body rhythm disruption it causes can be quite noticeable. For example, although the symptoms may only be subtle, for four days following landing at your destination you can expect psychomotor performance such as your hand-eye coordination to be affected. Similarly, for five days, your bowel and urinary function will in all likelihood be off schedule, making you very uncomfortable. Of course, *The Cure for Jet Lag* should render these symptoms virtually nonexistent. Follow the simple steps outlined below. Also, don't forget to refer to the Suggested Menus and Composition of Foods/Calorie Counter table in Chapter Twelve and the list of Major Influences on Body Clocks in Chapter Four.

FEAST = Generous servings FAST = Limited portions	
STEP #1	
THREE days before the flight	• Stop consuming beverages, food, or drugs containing methylated xanthines (coffee, tea, cocoa, chocolate, diet aids, etc.) in the early morning or late at night. • Feel free, however, to drink caffeinated beverages between 3 PM and 4:30 PM.
ONE day before the flight	• Eat a low-calorie HIGH-PROTEIN breakfast and a low-calorie HIGH-PROTEIN lunch. • Follow with a low-calorie HIGH-CARBOHYDRATE dinner. • Because this is a FAST day, keep the meals low in calories: a daily total of 800 is ideal. • Consume coffee or tea between 7 AM and 11 AM *only*.

STEP #2	
Morning of the flight	• Immediately upon rising (but no later than 11 AM) on the day of the flight drink TWO TO THREE CUPS of black coffee or strong, plain tea. • DO NOT consume any additional methylated xanthines today. • SET A WATCH TO DESTINATION TIME. • Begin STEP THREE with breakfast, destination time.

STEP #3

Day after the flight	• A half-hour before breakfast destination time, activate your body and mind (see Chapter Eleven, Mental and Physical Exercise Program).
	• This is a FEAST day, so eat a hearty, HIGH–PROTEIN breakfast and a hearty HIGH–PROTEIN lunch on destination time.
	• Follow with a hearty HIGH–CARBOHYDRATE dinner.
	• Light snacks after dinner are permissible.
	• Drink water all day to compensate for the dehydration that is common on flights.
	• Limit alcoholic beverages to no more than one drink (better yet, don't drink at all).
	• Since 8 PM destination time is midnight "old time," try to rest or sleep as soon as possible on destination time. Wear a sleep mask if necessary.
	Optional: For optimum energy, consider continuing the regimen of high-protein breakfasts and lunches, and high-carbohydrate dinners for the duration of your trip—until it is time to begin *The Cure for Jet Lag's* return-flight instructions. Also, keep in mind that your body clock is now set for destination time. From now on, if you drink caffeinated coffee or tea (except between 3 PM and 4:30 PM), you WILL feel the effects of sleepiness in the morning and sleeplessness at night.

WESTBOUND PHASE DELAY 5 or 6 TIME ZONES

degrees longitude E & W

From	To	# Zones	ml/km	Flight Time (h)
Honolulu [2]	Singapore [20]	6	6710/10797	11.6
Juneau [4]	Darwin [21.5]	6.5	7105/11432	12.3
Mexico City [6]	Wellington [24]	6	6899/11101	11.9
Cape Town [14]	Valparaiso [8]	6	4998/8042	8.6
Copenhagen [13]	Montreal [7]	6	3604/5799	6.2

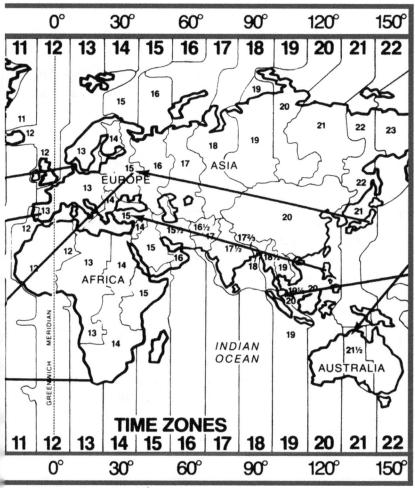

TIME ZONES

of Greenwich Meridian ⤏

From	To	# Zones	ml/km	Flight Time (h)
Moscow [15]	Buenos Aires [9]	6	8375/13476	14.5
Manila [20]	Istanbul [15]	5	5659/9106	9.8
Tokyo [21]	Moscow [15]	6	4657/7493	8.1
Chicago [6]	Wellington [24]	6	8349/13434	14.4
Madrid [13]	Miami [7]	6	4417/7107	7.6

Westbound 5-6 Time Zones

By anybody's definition, a five-hour to six-hour time change represents a major upheaval in body clocks. Your entire biochemistry will have to shift by a quarter of the twenty-four hour day. Sleeping, waking and eating schedules will all have to change to work with the new demands that will be placed on your body functions. Pay careful attention to the steps outlined below, however, and you will find your jet lag symptoms dramatically lessened, if not eliminated. Also, don't forget to refer to the Suggested Menus and Composition of Foods/Calorie Counter table in Chapter Twelve and the list of Major Influences on Body Clocks in Chapter Four.

FEAST = Generous servings FAST = Limited portions	
STEP #1	
THREE days before the flight	• Begin the System with a FEAST day by eating a hearty HIGH-PROTEIN breakfast and a hearty HIGH-PROTEIN lunch. • Follow with a hearty HIGH-CARBOHYDRATE dinner. • Stop consuming beverages, food, or drugs containing methylated xanthines (coffee, tea, cocoa, chocolate, diet aids, etc.) in the early morning or late at night. • Feel free, however, to consume caffeinated beverages between 3 PM and 4:30 PM.
TWO days before the flight	• Eat a low-calorie HIGH-PROTEIN breakfast, a low-calorie HIGH-PROTEIN lunch, and a low-calorie HIGH-CARBOHYDRATE dinner. • Because this is a FAST day, keep the meals low in calories; a daily total of 800 calories is ideal. • Do NOT eat any snacks after dinner.
ONE day before the flight	• Eat a hearty HIGH-PROTEIN breakfast and hearty HIGH-PROTEIN lunch. • Follow with a hearty HIGH-CARBOHYDRATE dinner. • Light snacks after dinner are permissible.

STEP #2
Morning of the flight   • On the day of the flight, sleep as late as possible.   • Immediately upon rising (but no later than 11 AM) on the day of the flight drink TWO TO THREE CUPS of black coffee or strong, plain tea.   • Do NOT consume additional methylated xanthines today.   • Eat a "late" low calorie HIGH-PROTEIN breakfast and a "late" low calorie HIGH-PROTEIN lunch.   • Follow with a "late" low calorie HIGH-CARBOHYDRATE dinner.   • Because this is a FAST day, keep the meals low in calories; a daily total of 800 calories is ideal.   • Do NOT eat any snacks after dinner.   • Drink water all day to compensate for the dehydration that is common on flights. Limit alcoholic beverages to no more than one drink (better yet, don't drink at all).   • RESET YOUR WRISTWATCH TO DESTINATION TIME.   • Since 6 PM destination time is midnight "old time," prepare for a long day. Try to rest or sleep on destination time only.

STEP #3
Breakfast destination time   • A half-hour before breakfast, destination time, activate your body and your brain (see Chapter Eleven, Mental and Physical Exercise Program).   • Eat a hearty HIGH-PROTEIN breakfast and a hearty HIGH-PROTEIN lunch on destination time.   • Follow with a hearty HIGH-CARBOHYDRATE dinner.   • Light snacks after dinner are permissible.   • Do NOT consume any methylated xanthines today.   • Turn in at a reasonable hour, destination time.   *Optional:* For optimum energy, consider continuing the regimen of high-protein breakfasts and lunches, and high-carbohydrate dinners for the duration of your trip—until it is time to begin *The Cure for Jet Lag's* return-flight instructions. Also, keep in mind that your body clock is now set for destination time. From now on, if you drink caffeinated coffee or tea (except between 3 PM and 4:30 PM), you WILL feel the effects of sleepiness in the morning and sleeplessness at night.

WESTBOUND PHASE DELAY 7 or 8 TIME ZONES

↖ degrees longitude E & W

From	To	# Zones	ml/km	Flight Time (h)
Nome [1]	Bombay [17.5]	7.5	5901/9495	10.2
Juneau [4]	Hong Kong [20]	8	5634/9065	9.7
Chicago [6]	Darwin [21.5]	8.5	9346/15038	16.1
Panama [7]	Wellington [24]	7	7433/11960	12.8
Cairo [14]	Chicago [6]	8	6103/9820	10.9

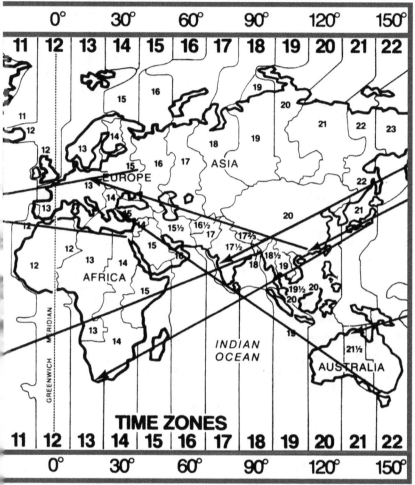

of Greenwich Meridian ↗

From	To	# Zones	ml/km	Flight Time (h)
Moscow [15]	Washington [7]	8	4883/7857	8.4
Calcutta [17.5]	Buenos Aires [9]	8.5	10242/16480	17.7
Hong Kong [20]	Berlin [13]	7	5500/8850	9.5
Tokyo [21]	Cape Town [14]	7	9071/14596	15.7
Melbourne [22]	Istanbul [15]	7	9088/14623	15.7

Westbound 7-8 Time Zones

A seven-hour to eight-hour westerly time zone change, like a seven-hour to eight-hour easterly time zone change, produces major body clock shifts in sleep and wake patterns. In order to assume destination time patterns immediately upon arrival, you should try to nap shortly after breakfast on the day of the time zone change because this time your nap represents an inactive period at your destination. Be aware that you are facing a very long day, seven or eight hours longer than your normal day. If you do not follow *The Cure for Jet Lag* and, instead, allow yourself to fall asleep at your usual time, you will suffer the consequences of severe jet lag. *The Cure for Jet Lag* will make it possible (and perhaps even painless) for you to assume your destination schedule immediately. Follow the simple steps outlined below. Also, don't forget to refer to the Suggested Menus and Composition of Foods/Calorie Counter table in Chapter Twelve and the list of Major Influences on Body Clocks in Chapter Four.

FEAST = Generous servings FAST = Limited portions	
STEP #1	
THREE days before the flight	• Begin the System with a FEAST day by eating a hearty HIGH-PROTEIN breakfast and a hearty HIGH-PROTEIN lunch. • Follow with a hearty HIGH-CARBOHYDRATE dinner. • STOP consuming beverages, foods, or drugs containing methylated xanthines (coffee, tea, cocoa, chocolate, diet aids, etc.) during the early morning or late evening. • Feel free to consume methylated xanthines between 3 PM and 4:30 PM *only.*
TWO days before the flight	• Eat a low-calorie HIGH-PROTEIN breakfast and a low-calorie HIGH-PROTEIN lunch. • Follow with a low-calorie HIGH-CARBOHYDRATE dinner. • Because this is a FAST day, keep the meals low in calories; a daily total of 800 calories is ideal. • Do NOT eat any snacks after dinner.
ONE day before the flight	• Eat a hearty HIGH-PROTEIN breakfast and a hearty HIGH-PROTEIN lunch. • Follow with a hearty HIGH-CARBOHYDRATE dinner. • Light snacks after dinner are permissible.

STEP #2	
Morning of the flight	• Sleep as late as possible. • Immediately upon rising (but no later than 11 AM) on the day of the flight drink TWO TO THREE CUPS of black coffee or strong, plain tea. • Do NOT consume any additional methylated xanthines today. • Eat a very "late" low-calorie HIGH-PROTEIN breakfast. This is your first and last meal based on your old schedule. A total of 250 calories is ideal. • Do NOT eat again until mealtime at your new destination, which, because of the time zone change, means you will be eating another breakfast in just a few hours. • Shortly after your late breakfast, rest, if possible, until your next meal, which is breakfast, destination time. • Drink water all day long to compensate for the dehydration that is common on flights. • Limit alcoholic beverages to no more than one drink (better yet, don't drink at all). • RESET YOUR WRISTWATCH TO DESTINATION TIME.

STEP #3	
Breakfast destination time	• A half-hour before breakfast, destination time, activate your body and your brain (see Chapter Eleven, Mental and Physical Exercise Program). • Eat a hearty, HIGH-PROTEIN breakfast and a hearty HIGH-PROTEIN lunch on destination time. • Follow with a hearty HIGH-CARBOHYDRATE dinner. • Light snacks after dinner are permissible. • Do NOT consume any methylated xanthines today. • Since 4 PM destination time is midnight "old time," prepare for a very long day. Keep active. Do NOT nap. Try to rest or sleep on destination time only. *Optional:* For optimum energy, consider continuing the regimen of high-protein breakfasts and lunches, and high-carbohydrate dinners for the duration of your trip—until it is time to begin *The Cure for Jet Lag's* return-flight instructions. Also, keep in mind that your body clock is now set for destination time. From now on, if you drink caffeinated coffee or tea (except between 3 PM and 4:30 PM), you WILL feel the effects of sleepiness in the morning and sleeplessness at night.

WESTBOUND PHASE DELAY 9 OR 10 TIME ZONES

degrees longitude E & W

From	To	# Zones	ml/km	Flight Time (h)
Nome [1]	Moscow [15]	10	4036/6494	7.0
Tel Aviv [14]	Spokane [4]	10	6685/10756	11.6
Murmansk [15]	Edmonton [5]	10	3800/6114	6.6
New Orleans [6]	Manila [20]	10	8742/14037	15.1
Washington [7]	Vladivostok [22]	9	6485/10435	11.2

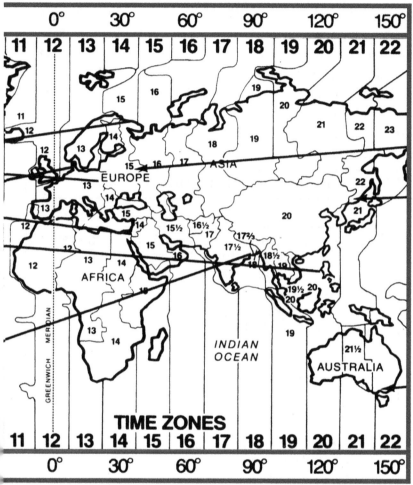

of Greenwich Meridian ➚

From	To	# Zones	ml/km	Flight Time (h)
Valparaiso [8]	Melbourne [22]	10	6998/11260	12.1
Buenos Aires [9]	Wellington [24]	9	6260/10073	10.8
Warsaw [13]	Juneau [4]	9	4680/7530	8.1
Copenhagen [13]	Los Angeles [4]	9	5612/9039	9.7
Calcutta [17.5]	Valparaiso [8]	9.5	10993/17688	19.0

Westbound 9-10 Time Zones

The same problems exist as with the other larger zone changes, but simply become more severe. To counter a very long day that entails being awake nine to ten hours longer than your normal schedule, you will need to grab as much rest during the flight day as possible, matching your enforced rest period to the inactive phase at your destination. You are going to need a great deal of energy to remain awake essentially for an entire day, but by following *The Cure for Jet Lag*, you should be able to fall into step with the local population quite easily. Follow the simple steps outlined below. Also, don't forget to refer to the Suggested Menus and Composition of Foods/Calorie Counter table in Chapter Twelve and the list of Major Influences on Body Clocks in Chapter Four.

FEAST = Generous servings FAST = Limited portions	
STEP #1	
THREE days before the flight	• Begin the System with a FEAST day by eating a hearty HIGH-PROTEIN breakfast and a hearty HIGH-PROTEIN lunch. • Follow with a hearty HIGH-CARBOHYDRATE dinner. • STOP consuming beverages, foods, or drugs containing methylated xanthines (coffee, tea, cocoa, chocolate, diet aids, etc.) during the early morning or late evening. • Feel free to consume methylated xanthines between 3 PM and 4:30 PM *only*.
TWO days before the flight	• Eat a low-calorie HIGH-PROTEIN breakfast and a low-calorie HIGH-PROTEIN lunch. • Follow with a low-calorie HIGH-CARBOHYDRATE dinner. • Because this is a FAST day, keep the meals low in calories; a daily total of 800 calories is ideal. • Do NOT eat any snacks after dinner.
ONE day before the flight	• Eat a hearty HIGH-PROTEIN breakfast and a hearty HIGH-PROTEIN lunch. • Follow with a hearty HIGH-CARBOHYDRATE dinner.

STEP #2	
Morning of the flight	• Sleep as late as possible. • Immediately upon rising (but no later than 11 AM) on the day of the flight drink TWO TO THREE CUPS of black coffee or strong, plain tea. • Do NOT consume any additional methylated xanthines today. • Eat a low calorie HIGH-PROTEIN breakfast. • Skip lunch. If you must eat, make it a low calorie HIGH-PROTEIN lunch. • Keep your meal(s) low in calories; *a total of 400 calories is ideal.* • Do NOT eat again until breakfast, destination time (only a few hours away due to the time change.) • Rest, if possible. • Drink water all day to compensate for the dehydration that is common on flights. • Limit alcoholic beverages to no more than one drink (better yet, don't drink at all). • RESET YOUR WRISTWATCH TO DESTINATION TIME.

STEP #3	
Breakfast destination time	• A half-hour before breakfast, destination time, activate your body and your brain (see Chapter Eleven, Mental and Physical Exercise Program). • Eat a hearty HIGH-PROTEIN breakfast and a hearty HIGH-PROTEIN lunch on destination time. • Follow with a hearty HIGH-CARBOHYDRATE dinner. • Light snacks after dinner are permissible. • Do NOT consume any methylated xanthines today. • Since 2 PM destination time is midnight "old time," prepare for a very long day. Keep active. • Do NOT nap. Try to rest or sleep on destination time only. *Optional:* For optimum energy, consider continuing the regimen of high-protein breakfasts and lunches, and high-carbohydrate dinners for the duration of your trip—until it is time to begin *The Cure for Jet Lag's* return-flight instructions. Also, keep in mind that your body clock is now set for destination time. From now on, if you drink caffeinated coffee or tea (except between 3 PM and 4:30 PM), you WILL feel the effects of sleepiness in the morning and sleeplessness at night.

Westbound 11-12 Time Zones

(See Eastbound 11-12 Time Zones in Chapter Seven, pages 88 – 91.) The 3-Step System is the same for eastbound and westbound 11-12 time zone changes.

CHAPTER NINE
COMPLEX FLIGHTS

Multi-Destination Flights and Multiple Time Zone Changes

Whether you are zigzagging across continents or flying in a consistent direction around the globe, *The Cure for Jet Lag* can be employed to great advantage. However, there are a number of variables that have to be taken into account, such as total overall length of the trip, the number of days in any given location and direction of flights, as well as how flexible your schedule is once you arrive at your destination. You will be able to derive enormous benefit from the 3-Step System's techniques with careful planning.

The following flights typically fall into the category "complex" because they include multiple stops in an easterly or westerly direction, and/or zigzagging flight patterns east to west and west to east, or vice versa.

Same direction
Short stay
Relatively brief length of stay

Zigzagging east to west and west to east
Short stay
Varying length of stay
Long length of stay

If you are going on a multi-destination flight, the first thing you should arrange is to have two wristwatches (you've got them in a bureau drawer somewhere!), or a companion who also wears a wristwatch. The next thing is to write down your itinerary, complete with approximate flying times, time changes involved in each flight, and the number of nights you will be spending in a specific destination.

Flights	Flying Time	Time Change	Nights at Destination
New York/Honolulu 11/30 10:50 AM–5:00 PM	11 hours	+ 5	2 nights
Honolulu/Manila 12/2 10:50 AM–7:25 AM	11 hours	+ 4	11 nights
Manila/Singapore 12/14 8:50 AM–6:15 PM	9 hours	0	4 nights

After you write down all the itinerary details, you will have a better idea of the type of approach to take in combating jet lag with *The Cure for Jet Lag*, and you will have a written reference for use during the actual trip.

Multi-Destination Flights, Same Direction—Short Stay

On short multi-destination flights in the same direction, you must decide whether you want to assume the time frame of your first destination or your second. You cannot do both; there simply is not enough time involved. For example, if you are traveling from Los Angeles to Hawaii for three days (time zone change -3) and then are going on to New Zealand for a total of three days (time zone change -2 from Hawaii), you could opt to synchronize your body clocks to Hawaii time and stay on Hawaii time when in New Zealand, or you could plan to assume New Zealand time throughout the entire trip. It is up to you. Both methods work more or less equivalently.

Again, do not forget to plan for a return trip to Los Angeles if you are going round trip. You must allow a sufficient number of days for the Preflight Steps of the 3-Step System.

Flights	Time Change	Nights at Destination
Los Angeles/Hawaii	-3	3 nights
Hawaii/New Zealand	-2	3 nights
New Zealand/Los Angeles	+5	returned

Multi-Destination Flights, Same Direction—Relatively Brief Length of Stay

On a multi-destination flight plan, adjust your body clocks to the destinations where you will stay the longest. For example, if you were flying from Chicago to India via Paris and Iran, and planned to spend only a few days in Paris, but a week or more in Iran, and then fly on to India for a day or two, your best bet would be to calculate the time zone changes from Chicago to Iran, and follow the 3-Step System as if you were not stopping in Paris at all. You would shift to Iran time during the Chicago-to-Paris flight, and while in Paris, stay on Iran time. Just do your best to impose Iran time on your activities.

Flights	Time Change	Nights at Destination
Chicago/Paris	+7	2 nights
Paris/Iran	+2.5	7 nights
Iran/India	+2	2 nights
India/Chicago	-11.5	returned

Stay on Iran time while you are in India. Do not forget if you plan to return to Chicago from India, initiate the appropriate 3-Step System, even if the best you can do is to start on the day of the return flight.

Multi-Destination Flights, East/West and West/East—Short Stay

Of course, the ideal approach is to allow sufficient time between time zone changes to prepare for each. However, in flights where you fly in a predominantly easterly or westerly direction, land for a brief one-day or two-day visit, and then take to the air again, heading in the reverse direction, it is best to remain on home time throughout the trip. Taking off one day from Egypt, landing in Thailand (time zone change +5), turning around a few days later to embark for Spain (time zone change -3 from Egypt), only to return to Egypt a day or two later, creates a tremendously debilitating effect on body clocks if you try to synchronize them to a new destination, only to demand another synchronization in another direction before the first attempt has been completed. A better approach would be to do your best to remain on hometown time throughout the trip if at all possible. If conflicts arise (meetings, tours, etc.), at least *try* to keep within the hometown time frame as much as possible.

Flights	Time Change	Nights at Destination
Egypt/Thailand	+5	2 nights
Thailand/Spain	-7	2 nights
Spain/Egypt	+3	returned

Multi-Destination Flights, East/West and West/East—Varying Length of Stay

There are a number of variables that have to be considered in multi-destination flights that zigzag around the world and involve a varying number of days at each destination. Ideally, it would be best to think in terms of extreme time zone changes, the amount of time involved in following *The Cure for Jet Lag*, and the number of days available at a destination for implementation. The following is an example of a flight that involves an east to west and west to east trip.

Flights	Time Change	Nights at Destination
New York/Honolulu	-6	2 nights
Honolulu/Manila	-6	11 nights
Manila/Singpore	0	4 nights
Singapore/Bali	0	5 nights
Bali/Hong Kong	0	4 nights
Hong Kong/Honolulu	+6	5 nights
Honolulu/San Francisco	+2	1 night
San Francisco/New York	+3	returned

Notice that you have eleven days in Honolulu, followed by some insignificant time zone changes at your next few destinations, followed by another major shift as you fly back to Honolulu, but combined with five nights for adjustment, and with a final combined total of five time zone changes from Honolulu through San Francisco to New York.

The best way to handle this flight pattern is to stay psychologically and physiologically on New York time during the first two days in Honolulu, but begin *The Cure for Jet Lag* in anticipation of commencing the Inflight Step while on the airplane to Manila. While in Singapore, Bali, and Hong Kong, just remain on local time, since it doesn't vary much from the time in Manila. Your eastbound flight from Hong Kong to Honolulu, however, involves another significant time zone change, so begin another set of Preflight Steps while still in Hong Kong, and implement the Inflight Steps while en route to Honolulu. Have a lovely, resynchronized five nights in Hawaii, and on the last few days of your stay, once again, start the Preflight Steps of the eastward-bound 3-Step System, breaking your fast on New York time, while still in San Francisco, and when you come down in New York, you should be ready to step right into the mainstream of activity with no problems.

Multi-Destination Flights, Any Direction—Long Length of Stay

A number of airlines offer fabulous flight-package arrangements. You buy a specific type of ticket that enables you to take as many flights as you desire, as long as you travel in essentially the same direction. Students, in particular, avail themselves of this type of flight package during the summer months, as do retirees and world travelers with a great deal of leisure time. With *The Cure for Jet Lag*, on trips that are going to require many weeks or months to complete, you will have the luxury of resynchronizing your body clocks to every destination upon arrival. When you have a few days before departure to begin the Preflight Steps, there is absolutely no reason to worry about wasting portions of your time with jet lag. On trips where scheduling is a little tight or virtually impossible, you must employ other measures that include superimposing one destination time on another. Not so, when you are traveling at your leisure.

Quite simply, write down your travel plans in the Itinerary Worksheet or fill it in as you go along. Start and stop *The Cure for Jet Lag* as you plan to leave for a new destination and as you arrive. Remember to allow sufficient time for the Preflight Steps.

Itinerary Worksheet

Flights	Flying Time	Time Change	Nights at Destination

CHAPTER TEN
FREQUENTLY ASKED QUESTIONS

You Bet You Have Questions!

When travelers who have followed *The Cure for Jet Lag* 3-Step System speak with other travelers who are just discovering that a cure for jet lag exists, invariably there are questions, particularly about the use of coffee or tea, drinking alcohol on the plane, and working the 3-Step System into the itinerary. Here are some of the typical questions you might ask if you were sitting next to someone on the plane and he or she was thumbing through a copy of *The Cure For Jet Lag*, carefully eating only the high-carbohydrate foods from an evening meal served inflight, and ordering two or three cups of black coffee or strong tea at 10 PM.

Q: What if I don't have three days before my flight in which to start the 3-Step System? A: If you only have two days before the flight, open *The Cure for Jet Lag* to the appropriate number of time zones crossed, east or west, and follow the preflight instructions for two days before the flight, switch to decaf coffee and tea, and avoid the foods that contain methylated xanthines found in certain foods and many drinks. If you are sitting on the airplane right now reading *The Cure for Jet Lag*, follow the instructions for the "inflight" portion of the 3-Step System right away. Following any part of the 3-Step System is better than not following *The Cure for Jet Lag* at all.

Q: Is there a treatment for caffeine withdrawal that will help me with my headache and fatique? A: Yes. According to Marshall Mandell, M.D., coauthor of the best-seller *5-Day Allergy Relief System*, if you are experiencing withdrawal symptoms, it will help to "take two tablets of Alka Seltzer Gold with two glasses of water: one tablet in each 8-ounce glass." Do not take the regular Alka Seltzer because it contains aspirin. If you read the Alka Seltzer Gold label, you'll see that it contains sodium bicarbonate and potassium bicarbonate with a few other ingredients. *Warning: If you have kidney disease or heart disease, these alkaline salts contain sodium and are not to be taken unless your physician permits you to do so. If you are pregnant or breast feeding, speak to your doctor.*

Q: Are you kidding? Drink two to three cups of black coffee or strong, plain tea, and then go to sleep on the plane? A: You probably won't fall sound asleep, and that's all right. The important thing is to relax. When you close your eyes and stop socializing, the chemical process that takes place in your body allows it to rest. Remember, the methylated xanthines are doing their job while you rest. Because of the methylated xanthines, when you enter the "active" phase of the system, you will be well on your way to being synchronized with the new time frame. Quiet rest is just as effective as actual sleep. You can initiate STEP #3 (breakfast, destination time) very soon after drinking the black coffee or tea required in STEP #2, or you can delay STEP #3 considerably. It all depends on how many time zones you cross and in what direction you are traveling. If you can't drink two to three cups, drink as much as you can. And if for some reason your physician doesn't want you drinking coffee at all, or coffee makes you ill, skip this step.

Q: Why can't I just drink a few glasses of my favorite Scotch and call it a night? A: The information about the effect of alcohol on body clocks is somewhat inconclusive. Until more evidence is in, the best approach would be not to drink alcohol at all, or to drink very little while on the airplane. Alcohol does tend to make you dehydrated, and red wine, sherry and port have histamines in them that can cause head congestion. And alcohol has a bigger kick because of the cabin's atmospheric pressures.

Q: On the fast/eating lightly days, must I eat everything offered and as much as outlined? A: No, you may eat even less. The idea behind the fast days is to keep the caloric content down to a maximum of 800 calories. The high-protein breakfasts and lunches insure a high energy level throughout the day despite the reduction in calories, and the high-carbohydrate suppers will actually help you sleep at night.

Q: Do I really have to eat large meals on the feast days? A: Yes. A few thousand calories is ideal if you can, but the amount of food you will be able to consume will depend greatly upon your own build and metabolism.

Q: I'm not a breakfast eater. What should I do? A: It is all right to miss breakfast on the fast days and the feast days, but be sure not to skip breakfast on the day of your arrival at your destination. You must eat a high-protein meal in order to signal your central nervous system that a new time frame has begun. If you do skip breakfast on preflight and inflight days and begin to feel a little weak, eat an egg or drink a glass of milk (high in protein) to give you some energy. Take a look at some of the suggested menus in Chapter Twelve.

Q: Why am I only allowed to have coffee, tea, or caffeinated sodas between 3 PM and 4:30 PM? A: Your body chemistry reacts differently to methylated xanthines over the course of a day. For reasons not yet fully understood, if taken in the morning, methylated xanthines have the ability to set body clocks back, and if taken at night, ahead. If taken in the afternoon, "British tea-time," methylated xanthines seem to have little or no effect on the timing of body clocks.

Q: May I drink decaffeinated coffee and tea? A: Sure! Have as much as you want at any time of the day or night. Since decaffeination removes the methylated xanthines, even though there may be a small amount of caffeine in decaffeinated beverages, you don't have to worry about any effect on your body clock.

Q: What about sugar or sugar substitutes in my coffee or tea? A: Sugar-free substitutes are fine, but do not add real sugar or real cream to your coffee when *The Cure for Jet Lag* calls for plain, unsweetened coffee or tea.

Q: What if I have to change flights, or get delayed. Does this throw the 3-Step System off? A: Absolutely not. It does not matter if your flight is delayed on takeoff or landing, or if you have a layover for a few hours. Just stick to the Preflight, Inflight and Postflight steps the best you can. If your layover is for several days, however, and you will be changing time zones again, select the 3-Step System for your first destination (more about this in Chapter Nine). Depending upon how many time zones you have crossed, you'll wind up spending several jet-lag-free or jet-lag-reduced days at your first stop. In anticipation of your next flight out, you would be wise to avoid any caffeinated beverages until takeoff. If you must drink coffee or tea, only drink it between the hours of 3 PM and 4:30 PM when the methylated zanthines have no effect. Fast on the day of your second flight, and follow the appropriate Preflight, Inflight and Postflight steps based on the number of time zones crossed during the second flight.

Frequently Asked Questions

Q: I cannot tolerate coffee or tea in any amount whatsoever. Must I include them in the 3-Step System? A: The methylated xanthines are extremely important, but if you simply cannot tolerate even one cup of coffee, a half-cup of coffee or a few sips of plain tea, then skip it. At the hour you are supposed to have the beverage, don't drink anything at all (of course, water is fine). Don't substitute other caffinated foods, beverages or drugs. They will contain other ingredients that you must avoid at this time. Fast until breaking-the-fast at destination time.

Q: Would it help me sleep if I took a mild sedative after I drank my two to three cups of coffee? Is it a good idea to take a sleeping pill or tranquilizer on the night of my arrival at my destination? A: No and no. Because your body must work overtime to eliminate drugs from your system, you would be introducing a factor that would confuse the orderly resetting of your body clocks.

Q: Will taking a nonprescription stimulant on the day of my arrival help? A: No. Many nonprescription stimulants like Dexatrim and No-Doz have a caffeine base. Their use will confuse your body clocks and you will negate the "clock-setting" effect of the caffeine you consumed earlier.

Q: What about melatonin? It's supposed to be a magic pill. A: It would be great if you could pop a pill and call it a foolproof solution to jet lag. Unfortunately, melatonin can cause sleepiness, lethargy, confusion and decreased mental sharpness, exactly the effects that *The Cure for Jet Lag* is designed to combat. Moreover, the dosage regimen is so complicated that even Jane E. Brody, Personal Health columnist for *The New York Times* said she "gave up the dosing schedule within two days" on her trip to Australia. In a study in 2000 to determine the "effects of oral melatonin in alleviating jet lag by investigating its effects on subjects who had flown from London to Eastern Australia, 10 time zones to the east," the Research Institute for Sport and Exercise Sciences in the United Kingdom found "melatonin had no benefit in alleviating jet lag or the components of jet lag, and it did not influence the process of phase adjustment." In addition, no one knows what the long-term effects might be. Long story short: you don't need it for the 3-Step System to be tremendously effective. So why bother with melatonin?

Q: Is it true that Viagra reduces jet lag? A: Yes, so laboratory hamsters say, according to The National Academy of Sciences, but only for simulated eastbound flights from New York to Paris. Stick to the simple 3-Step System. It's all-natural. It works just fine without Viagra.

Q: Will it be difficult to get high-protein breakfasts and lunches, and high-carbohydrate suppers while on the airplane? A: Some airlines on some flights have a special service for passengers with special food requirements: low-sodium, vegetarian, kosher, etc. If a particular meal that is served is not limited to strictly high-protein or high-carbohydrate foods, pick and choose among the foods offered. At lunch, for example, you may need to reject the roll, but certainly not the entire meal.

Q: Should I brown bag it? A: If you are on a no-frills, no-food flight, you should be able to "brown bag" it in a clear container. However, the Transportation Security Administration has rules about what a passenger may carry on the plane. But these rules are constantly changing. Moreover, individual airlines sometimes impose their own rules, not to mention the fact that individual security personnel may act arbitrarily.

Q: Why can't I take a nap on the first day at my destination if I feel a little tired? A: No naps! The idea is to get right into the time frame of your destination. True, studies have shown that a nap is refreshing, although no one is quite sure why. (It is guessed that a break in conscious thought, an escape from anxiety or pressures, etc., may be the reason.) However, a nap can disrupt sleep patterns later at night. Since you want to be sure to get a good night's sleep on your first night, avoid the impulse to nap.

Q: How soon after my flight has touched down may I drink caffeinated coffee or tea as often as I want? A: Because caffeinated coffee or plain tea jolt your body clocks ahead or backward in time, except between the hours between of 3 PM and 4:30 PM, limit your coffee or tea intake to those hours for at least the first couple of days after landing, if not for the duration of your trip. If you do resume drinking caffeinated coffee in the morning or at night, you will feel the dramatic effects of the methylated xanthines on your now regulated body clocks as you knock them out of sync.

Q: What shall I do if my business meeting takes place in Germany, and then I have another business meeting a day or two later in Tokyo? How can I start a system for Frankfurt, get to Frankfurt, and then have to go on before I have had enough time to implement a new system for my next appointment? A: Before you agree to these appointments, you should give the timing for the 3-Step System some serious thought. In this case, your options are:

1. To reschedule enough time between appointments to enable you to implement the 3-Step System again before you leave Germany,

2. To remain on Frankfurt time during your Tokyo appointment, or

3. To remain on your hometown time throughout the trip.

Any course other than these three would have you at a distinct disadvantage in negotiation and decision-making abilities. Take a look at Chapter Nine, Complex Flights.

Q: I am on a restricted diet. What should I do? A: The key to the meals in the 3-Step System is their composition and their timing. The 3-Step System consists of high-protein breakfasts and high-protein lunches, followed by high-carbohydrate suppers. If you cannot follow *The Cure for Jet Lag* exactly and must modify it, consult with your doctor and explain the mealtime approach. See what he or she says.

CHAPTER ELEVEN

MENTAL AND PHYSICAL EXERCISE PROGRAM

Rise and Shine on Destination Time!

During some of the longer flights to a new time zone, *The Cure for Jet Lag* calls for periods of sleep or rest. At that time you should cease talking to your neighbor, close your book, turn off your computer, or turn away from the inflight movie.

Once you have settled under a warm blanket and closed your eyes, your body will begin to slow down. Within a few minutes your heart rate will drop ten to twenty beats per minute. Without blood circulating vigorously throughout your body and brain, your temperature will begin to fall, your muscles and joints will stiffen and lose their elasticity, and your conscious mind will become sluggish. As you rest in your airplane seat, your legs, feet, and hands will swell slightly as gravity pulls the fluids in your body to your extremities.

After this rest period, *The Cure for Jet Lag* requires a few minutes of mental and physical exercise to bring your body and mind back to optimal functioning and alertness.

Waking Your Body Up in Time for a New Time Zone

In order to follow the physical exercise aspect of *The Cure for Jet Lag*, you must *get up* and *get moving*. If you just remain seated in your chair, you will not be able to stimulate your heart so that your blood will begin to circulate rapidly, loosening up your joints and clearing your mind.

The following are a few physical exercises that can be done in the aisle, the rear of the plane, or in the lavatories. You should perform the exercises diligently in order to derive maximum benefits. (If you have back trouble or any physical ailment that will prevent you from exercising, check with your physician about participating in this aspect of the 3-Step System. Try to get substitute exercises.)

1. Take five deep breaths to pump your lungs full of oxygen and change the "tidal" air that is always in the bottom of your lungs.

2. Stand up on your toes and s-t-r-e-t-c-h for the ceiling. Repeat five to ten times.

3. Rotate your shoulders in both directions—left shoulder five times forward, five times backward; right shoulder five times forward, five times backward. Then rotate both shoulders simultaneously forward and backward.

4. Rotate your head—twice to the right, twice to the left. Repeat five times.

5. Bend backward from the waist, chin pointed toward the ceiling. Repeat five times.

6. Rotate your wrists and ankles. Repeat ten times.

7. Pull your knees up to your waist. Repeat five times for each leg.

For additional exercises perform a web search for "inflight exercises." Also, some airlines provide inflight exercise videos.

Now, if you are not already thinking about a trip to the lavatory, or are not already there, go and tidy up, comb your hair, and splash cool water on your face. This step will also signal your body and mind that the day has, indeed, begun.

Waking Your Mind Up in Time for a New Time Zone

Your blood is circulating, your muscles are stretched, and your joints are rotating smoothly. It is time to "flex" your mind and get it operating at peak performance.

1. If you are with friends or family or have made the acquaintance of seat companions or airplane personnel, dust off the mental cobwebs acquired during rest or sleep through stimulating conversation or a fast-moving game of cards that requires *concentration.*

2. If you do not want to talk with anyone sitting next to you (actually, if they are not participating in *The Cure for Jet Lag*, they may well be asleep and/or feeling the ill-effects of lack of rest or sleep), and you have an interesting book to read, do so. Or, if you have work to do, begin it. Work on something that requires concentration so that you do not drift back to sleep.

If you follow the advice in this chapter for mental and physical exercise, you will find that you are ready to begin a new day . . . on a new schedule . . . in a new time zone.

CHAPTER TWELVE

3-STEP SYSTEM PREFLIGHT, INFLIGHT AND POSTFLIGHT MEALS & MENUS

Feasting and Fasting (Eating Lightly)

On feast days before the flight, remember to eat like you would at Thanksgiving. Really pack in the food. Try and consume several thousand calories. On fast days, including day-of-the-flight—which is always a fast day—dramatically reduce your caloric intake. Consume 800 calories or less. Because high protein meals provide many hours of energy, even at reduced calorie levels while on the fast, create meals with high-protein content at breakfast and lunch, but not at dinner. At dinner, make predominantly high-carbohydrate foods so that you will have a burst of energy that will quickly fade by the time you to go to bed.

Suggested Menus	
FAST Day Approximate Caloric Content = (800)	
Breakfast:	
1 egg, any style	82
1/2 cup low-fat pot cheese or low-fat cottage cheese	86
1/2 cup of orange juice	60
Total calories	**228**
or	
2 eggs, any style	164
1/2 piece of lightly buttered toast	50
Total calories	**214**

Suggested Menus	
FAST Day (cont.) Approximate Caloric Content = (800)	
Lunch:	
1/2 cup water-packed tuna or salmon with lemon juice	144
1 piece of bread, lightly buttered or with a light coat of mayonnaise	65
A few slices of tomato and a few leaves of lettuce	20
1/4 cup low-fat or skim milk	75
Total calories	**304**
or	
1 chicken breast, skin removed	154
1 cup bouillon	5
1/2 cup of low-fat pot cheese or cottage cheese	86
Total calories	**245**
Dinner:	
Medium-sized plate of combination salad—lettuce, tomato, cucumber, onion, green pepper, radish, celery	120
1 tbsp. salad dressing, any kind	50
1 piece of bread, lightly buttered	65
1 alcoholic beverage (optional)	100
1 apple or pear	50
Total calories	**385**
or	
1 small bowl of pasta, lightly buttered with margarine	150
1 piece of bread, lightly buttered	65
1 cup cooked vegetables—string beans, summer squash, carrots, broccoli	40
1 alcoholic beverage (optional)	100
Total calories	**355**

Suggested Menus	
FEAST Day (Eat large quantities at every meal! Enjoy!)	

Breakfast:

Plenty of steak and eggs or ham and cheese

As much milk as you want

1/2 cup orange juice

1 piece of bread, lightly buttered

Total calories	Unlimited

or

A very large omelet, made with any ingredients—cheeses, vegetables

As much milk as you like

1 cup orange juice

1 piece of bread, lightly buttered

Total calories	Unlimited

Lunch:

Lots of assorted cold cuts—chicken, turkey, lean meat, tongue

Assorted cheeses—any type and as much as you like

As much milk as you like

1 piece of bread, lightly buttered

1 cup vegetables—cauliflower, string beans, carrots

1 apple, pear, banana, bunch of grapes

Total calories	Unlimited

or

Lots of meat, fish, fowl

Baked beans, lima beans

Slices of cheese, any kind, any amount

1 piece of bread, lightly buttered

1 apple, tangerine, cherries

Total calories	Unlimited

129

Suggested Menus		
FEAST Day (cont.) (Eat large quantities at every meal! Enjoy!)		
Dinner:		
Pasta with a meatless tomato sauce, as much as you want		
Bread, lightly buttered		
Fruit salad, as much as you want of any fruit		
Cake, cookies		
Alcoholic beverages in reasonable amounts		
	Total calories	**Unlimited**
or		
Sauteed vegetables—potatoes, corn, green beans, onions, squash		
Mixed salad—as much as you want		
Salad dressing, any kind		
Bread, lightly buttered		
Cake, cookies		
Alcoholic beverages in reasonable amounts		
	Total calories	**Unlimited**

Selecting the Right Foods for Postflight Meals

Since specific combinations of foods play a major role in eliminating chronic fatigue, ensuring lots of energy, and activating your body clock on the first day of arrival at your destination, you need to be prepared to follow through at your destination with a high-protein breakfast and high-protein lunch, followed by a high-carbohydrate dinner regimen.

The Composition of Foods/Calorie Counter that follows is based primarily on United States Department of Agriculture tables. They are a reliable guide to follow in formulating the high-protein breakfasts and lunches and high-carbohydrate suppers that are a crucial part of *The Cure for Jet Lag*. Divided into columns representing caloric, protein, fat, and carbohydrate content, this section should provide you with all the information you need, whether at home or abroad, for developing your own menus.

If you are in doubt when consulting a foreign menu about the ingredients in a specific dish, ask the waiter to explain them to you. When the 3-Step System calls for high-protein meals, try to avoid rich sauces and condiments, which may well contain large amounts of oils and sugars, respectively.

When the system requires high-carbohydrate meals, realize that meat or cheese in any quantity have the power to change your body chemistry and promote energy—the last thing you want just prior to going to bed. Know what you are eating and why.

Yes, it takes a little investigation to determine the actual composition of meals, especially when a meal has many ingredients, but with a little perseverance and a little planning ahead of time, you should not have any trouble keeping your meals within the requirements of *The Cure for Jet Lag.*

COMPOSITION OF FOODS/CALORIE COUNTER

	Calories	Protein (grams)	Fat (grams)	Carbohydrates (grams)
MEATS AND POULTRY (3 1/2 ounce servings)				
Bacon, crisp, drained:				
2 slices	86	5	8	1
Beef, cooked:				
Lean and fat	286	27	19	0
Lean only	196	31	7	0
Hamburger, broiled:				
Regular ground	286	24	20	0
Lean ground	219	27	12	0
Rib:				
Lean and fat	440	19	39	0
Lean only	241	28	13	0
Round:				
Lean and fat	261	28	15	0
Lean only	189	31	6	0
Steak, sirloin:				
Lean and fat	387	23	3	0
Lean only	207	32	8	0
Steak, porterhouse:				
Lean and fat	465	20	42	0
Lean only	224	30	11	0
Steak, T-bone:				
Lean and fat	473	20	43	0
Lean only	223	30	10	0

Composition of Foods

	Calories	Protein (grams)	Fat (grams)	Carbohydrates (grams)
MEATS AND POULTRY (3 1/2 ounce servings)				
Steak, club:				
Lean and fat	454	21	41	0
Lean only	244	30	13	0
Beef, corned:				
Cooked, medium fat	372	23	30	0
Canned, lean	185	26	8	0
Beef liver, fried	229	26	11	5
Cooked without fat	140	20	4	6
Beef tongue:				
Cooked, braised	244	22	17	trace
Canned or pickled	267	19	20	trace
Chicken, cooked:				
Broilers:				
Light meat, skinless	166	32	3	0
Dark meat, skinless	176	28	6	0
Roasters:				
Light meat, skinless	182	32	5	0
Dark meat, skinless	184	29	7	0
Canned, boneless	198	29	7	0
Livers, simmered	165	27	4	3
Lamb, choice grade:				
Leg:				
Lean and fat	279	25	19	0
Lean only	186	29	7	0
Loin:				
Lean and fat	359	22	29	0
Lean only	188	28	8	0
Shoulder:				
Lean and fat	338	22	27	0
Lean only	205	27	10	0
Pork, fresh: composite of trimmed, lean cuts:				
Medium fat class	373	23	31	0
Lean only	236	28	13	0
Chop, thick, with bone	260	16	21	0
Roast, oven-cooked:				
Lean and fat	310	21	24	0
Lean only	175	20	10	0
Pork, cured:				
Ham, medium fat:				
Cooked, roasted	289	21	22	0
Lean only	187	25	9	0

	Calories	Protein (grams)	Fat (grams)	Carbohydrates (grams)
MEATS AND POULTRY (3 1/2 ounce servings)				
Sausage:				
Bologna, all meat	277	13	23	4
Braunschweiger	319	15	27	2
Brown-and-serve	422	17	38	3
Country style	345	15	31	0
Deviled ham, canned	351	14	32	0
Frankfurters	304	12	27	2
Knockwurst	278	14	23	2
Liverwurst, smoked	319	15	27	2
Boiled ham, luncheon meat	234	19	17	0
Polish-style sausage	304	16	26	1
Pork sausage, links	476	18	44	trace
Salami, dry	450	24	38	1
Sweetbreads:				
Beef	320	26	23	0
Calf	168	33	3	0
Lamb	175	28	6	0
Turkey:				
Flesh and skin, roasted	223	32	10	0
Light meat, skinless	176	33	4	0
Dark meat, skinless	203	30	8	0
Veal:				
Average cut, braised, lean and fat	235	28	13	0
Cutlet, boneless, broiled	185	23	9	4
Round, with rump	216	27	11	0
FISH AND SHELLFISH (3 1/2 ounce servings)				
Abalone, canned	80	16	3	2
Anchovy, canned, 3 filets	21	3	1	trace
Bass, black sea, poached or broiled or baked	93	19	1	trace
Bass, striped, baked or stuffed	80	16	3	2
Bluefish, baked, broiled, fried	205	23	10	5
Clams:				
Raw, meat only	76	13	2	2
Canned, drained	98	16	3	2
Cod, broiled	170	29	5	9

Composition of Foods

	Calories	Protein (grams)	Fat (grams)	Carbohydrates (grams)
FISH AND SHELLFISH (3 1/2 ounce servings)				
Crab, Dungeness, rock, and king	93	17	2	trace
Flounder, baked	202	30	8	0
Haddock	165	20	6	6
Halibut, broiled	171	25	7	0
Herring, raw:				
Atlantic	176	17	12	0
Pacific	98	18	3	0
Pickled	223	20	15	0
Salted or brined	218	19	15	0
Kippered	211	22	13	0
Lobster, northern, canned or cooked	95	19	2	trace
Mackerel:				
Canned	183	20	11	0
Salted	305	19	25	0
Smoked	219	24	13	0
Mussels, meat only	95	14	2	4
Ocean perch, fried	277	19	13	7
Oysters, raw:				
Eastern	66	8	2	3
Western	91	11	2	6
Fried	239	9	14	19
Roe, baked or broiled cod and shad	126	22	3	2
Salmon:				
Cooked, broiled or baked	182	27	7	0
Smoked	176	22	9	0
Scallops, bay and sea, steamed	112	23	1	0
Shad, baked	201	23	11	0
Shrimp, canned, meat only	116	24	1	1
Sole, baked	202	30	8	0
Swordfish, broiled	174	28	6	0
Tuna, canned:				
Packed in oil, drained	197	29	8	0
Packed in water	170	15	11	4
Weakfish, broiled	208	25	11	0
Whitefish, lake, smoked	155	21	7	0

	Calories	Protein (grams)	Fat (grams)	Carbohydrates (grams)
FRUIT AND FRUIT PRODUCTS (1/2 cup except where otherwise noted)				
Apples, 1 medium	70	trace	trace	18
Applesauce, fresh	60	trace	0	15
Applesauce, canned:				
Sweetened	91	trace	trace	24
Unsweetened	41	trace	trace	11
Apricots:				
Canned, heavy syrup	86	trace	trace	22
Dried, uncooked	332	6	1	85
Cooked, sweetened fruit				
and liquid	122	1	trace	31
Banana, 1 medium	85	1	trace	22
Blackberries, raw	58	1	1	13
Blueberries, raw	62	1	1	15
Cantaloupe, raw, 1/2 melon	40	1	trace	9
Cherries, raw, sweet	70	1	1	17
Cranberries				
Canned, sweetened	146	trace	trace	38
Juice, cocktail, canned	65	trace	trace	17
Figs, dried, 1 medium	60	1	trace	15
Grapefruit, raw, white:				
1/2 medium	41	trace	trace	11
Juice, fresh	41	1	trace	10
Canned, unsweetened	43	1	trace	10
Frozen concentrate, water added	44	1	trace	11
Grapes, seedless, green	69	1	1	16
Grape juice, bottled	66	trace	trace	17
Mandarin oranges, canned w/syrup	50	1	trace	12
Nectarine, 1 medium	64	1	trace	17
Orange, 1 medium	60	2	trace	13
Orange juice:				
Fresh	45	1	trace	10
Frozen concentrate, water added	45	1	trace	11
Peaches:				
Fresh, 1 medium	33	1	trace	8
Canned, heavy syrup	96	trace	trace	25
Water packaged	75	1	trace	19
Nectar, canned	48	trace	trace	12

Composition of Foods

	Calories	Protein (grams)	Fat (grams)	Carbohydrates (grams)
FRUIT AND FRUIT PRODUCTS (1/2 cup except where otherwise noted)				
Pears:				
Fresh, 1 medium	100	1	1	24
Canned, heavy syrup	76	trace	trace	12
Nectar, canned	52	trace	trace	13
Pineapple:				
Fresh, 1/2 cup	52	trace	trace	14
Canned, syrup	58	trace	trace	15
Canned, unsweetened	55	trace	trace	13
Plums:				
Fresh, 1 medium	30	trace	trace	7
Canned, syrup	83	trace	trace	22
Prunes:				
Dried, 4 medium	80	1	trace	19
Juice, canned	77	trace	trace	19
Raisins, dried	289	3	trace	77
Raspberries:				
Red, raw	57	1	1	14
Frozen, sweetened	98	1	trace	25
Strawberries:				
Fresh	37	1	1	8
Frozen, sweetened	109	1	trace	28
Tangerines:				
Fresh, 1 medium	46	1	trace	12
Juice, canned, unsweetened	43	1	trace	10
Frozen concentrate, water added	46	1	trace	11
Watermelon, 1 slim slice	26	1	trace	6
VEGETABLES (1/2 cup except where otherwise noted)				
Artichoke, cooked	44	3	trace	10
Asparagus, 6 spears	20	2	trace	3
Avocado, large, 1/2	180	2	17	6
Beans:				
Green, cooked	25	2	trace	6
Wax, cooked	22	2	trace	5
Lima, cooked	111	8	1	20
Red kidney	90	6	trace	16
Beets, cooked	32	1	trace	7
Broccoli, cooked	26	3	trace	5

	Calories	Protein (grams)	Fat (grams)	Carbohydrates (grams)
VEGETABLES (1/2 cup except where otherwise noted)				
Cabbage:				
Raw	25	1	trace	5
Cooked	20	1	trace	4
Carrots, diced, raw	42	1	1	10
Cauliflower, cooked	22	2	trace	4
Celery, diced, raw	17	1	trace	4
Corn:				
5" ear	65	2	1	16
Cream style	82	2	trace	20
Canned, with liquid	66	2	1	16
Cucumber:				
Fresh, 1 medium	16	1	trace	3
Pickle, sweet, 1 medium	146	1	trace	37
Pickle, sour or dill, 1 large	11	1	trace	22
Eggplant, cooked	19	1	trace	4
Kale, cooked	39	5	1	6
Kohlrabi, cooked	24	2	trace	5
Lentils, cooked	106	8	trace	19
Lettuce, 2 large leaves	5	1	trace	trace
Mushrooms:				
Cooked or canned	17	2	trace	2
Raw	28	3	trace	4
Okra, cooked, 8 pods	29	2	trace	6
Olives:				
Green, 1 large	9	trace	1	trace
Ripe, 1 large	13	trace	2	trace
Onions:				
Mature, raw	38	2	trace	9
Cooked	29	1	trace	7
Parsnips, cooked	66	2	1	15
Peas, green:				
Cooked	71	5	trace	12
Canned, drained	88	5	trace	17
Frozen, cooked, drained	68	5	trace	12
Peppers, sweet, green, 1 medium	22	1	trace	5
Potatoes, 1 medium:				
Baked, skinless	90	3	trace	21
Boiled	105	3	trace	23

Composition of Foods

	Calories	Protein (grams)	Fat (grams)	Carbohydrates (grams)
VEGETABLES (1/2 cup except where otherwise noted)				
Potatoes, 1 medium:				
French fried, 10 pieces	155	2	7	20
Mashed, with milk	65	2	1	13
Chips, 10 pieces	110	1	7	10
Radishes, 4 small	10	trace	trace	2
Sauerkraut, canned	18	1	trace	2
Spinach, cooked	26	3	trace	4
Squash, cooked:				
Summer, diced	14	1	trace	3
Winter, baked	63	2	trace	15
Frozen, cooked, drained	63	2	trace	15
Sweet potatoes, 1 medium:				
Baked	155	2	1	36
Boiled	170	2	1	39
Candied	295	2	6	60
Tomatoes:				
Raw, sliced, 1 medium	22	1	trace	5
Canned or cooked, 1/2 cup	22	1	trace	5
Juice, 1/2 cup	19	1	trace	4
Catsup, 1 tbsp.	15	trace	trace	4
Turnips, cooked, diced	23	1	trace	5
Vegetable juice cocktail, 6 oz.	31	2	trace	7
Vegetables, mixed, cooked, drained	64	3	trace	13
CHEESE, CREAM, MILK, EGGS, AND RELATED PRODUCTS (1 ounce unless otherwise noted)				
Cheese:				
American	106	6	9	1
Blue	100	6	8	1
Brie	95	6	8	trace
Camembert	85	6	7	trace
Cheddar	114	7	10	1
Cottage:				
Creamed, 1/2 cup	117	14	5	4
Uncreamed, 1/2 cup	96	20	1	2
Cream	99	2	10	1
Edam	101	7	8	1
Feta	75	4	6	1
Fontina	110	7	9	1
Gouda	101	7	8	1

	Calories	Protein (grams)	Fat (grams)	Carbohydrates (grams)
CHEESE, CREAM, MILK, EGGS, AND RELATED PRODUCTS (1 ounce unless otherwise noted)				
Cheese:				
Limburger	93	6	8	trace
Monterey jack	106	7	9	trace
Mozzarella	80	6	6	1
Muenster	104	7	9	1
Parmesan, grated, 1 tbsp.	111	10	8	1
Pot cheese:				
Low fat 2%, 1/2 cup	101	16	2	4
Low fat 1%, 1/2 cup	82	14	1	3
Port du Salut	100	7	8	trace
Ricotta, 1/2 cup	216	14	16	4
Romano	110	9	8	1
Roquefort	105	6	9	1
Swiss:				
Natural, domestic	107	8	8	4
Processed	95	7	7	1
Cheese spread, American	82	5	6	3
Cream, 1 tbsp.:				
Half-and-half	20	1	2	1
Light	29	1	3	1
Medium	37	1	4	1
Heavy	26	trace	3	trace
Sour	26	1	3	1
Creamer, nondairy, 1 tsp.	11	trace	1	1
Milk, fresh, 1 cup:				
Skim	72	7	trace	10
Skimmed partially, 2% fat	118	8	2	12
Whole, 3.7% fat	132	7	8	10
Yogurt, 1/2 cup:				
Plain, low fat	50	3	2	5
Whole milk	62	3	3	5
Eggs, chicken, 1 large boiled	97	6	6	1
GRAIN PRODUCTS: BREADS, CEREALS, GRAINS, CAKES				
Biscuits, 1 medium	138	3	7	17
Bran flakes, 1/2 cup	303	10	2	81
Breads, 1 slice:				
Cracked wheat	60	2	1	12
French	58	2	1	11
Italian	55	2	trace	11

Composition of Foods

	Calories	Protein (grams)	Fat (grams)	Carbohydrates (grams)
GRAIN PRODUCTS: BREADS, CEREALS, GRAINS, CAKES				
Breads, 1 slice:				
Protein	45	3	0	9
Pumpernickel	56	2	trace	12
Raisin	60	2	1	12
Rye, light	55	2	trace	12
White, enriched	60	2	1	12
Whole wheat	55	2	1	11
Cakes, 1 medium slice:				
Angel food	110	3	trace	23
Apple Brown Betty	151	2	4	30
Chocolate fudge	420	5	14	70
Cupcake, plain	160	3	3	31
Fruit cake	105	2	4	17
Poundcake	130	2	7	16
Sponge cake	148	3	6	25
Cookies, plain, 1 medium	110	2	3	19
Cornbread	207	7	7	29
Cornflakes, enriched, 1 cup	93	2	trace	21
Corn muffins, 1 medium	155	4	5	22
Corn, puffed, presweetened, enriched, 1/2 cup	379	4	trace	90
Crackers, 2 medium:				
Graham	55	1	1	10
Saltines	35	1	1	6
Soda, plain	45	1	1	8
Donuts, plain, 1 medium	135	2	7	17
Macaroni, cooked, 1 cup	155	5	1	32
Melba toast, 1 slice	15	1	trace	3
Muffin, enriched, white flour, 1 medium	135	4	5	19
Noodles, cooked, 1 cup	200	7	2	37
Oatmeal, cooked, 1 cup	55	2	1	10
Pancakes, 1 medium	60	2	2	8
Pie, 1 medium slice:				
Apple	330	3	13	53
Custard	265	7	11	34
Lemon meringue	300	4	12	45
Mince	340	3	9	62
Pumpkin	265	5	12	34

	Calories	Protein (grams)	Fat (grams)	Carbohydrates (grams)
GRAIN PRODUCTS: BREADS, CEREALS, GRAINS, CAKES				
Popcorn, 1 cup	55	2	1	11
Rice, 1/2 cup:				
White, parboiled	100	4	trace	22
Puffed, enriched	25	trace	trace	6
Rolls, 1 medium	115	3	2	20
Rye wafers, 2 medium	45	2	trace	10
Spaghetti, cooked 1/2 cup	75	3	trace	16
Wheat, puffed, enriched, 1/2 cup:				
Plain, unsweetened	363	15	2	79
Presweetened	376	6	2	88
Wheat, shredded, plain, 1/2 cup	354	10	2	80
Wheat germ, 1 tbsp.	24	12	1	3
FATS, OILS, AND SHORTENINGS				
Butter, 1 pat	36	trace	4	trace
Margarine, 1 pat	36	trace	4	trace
Oils, salad or cooking, 1 tbsp.	125	0	14	0
Salad dressings, 1 tbsp.:				
Blue cheese	90	1	10	1
French	60	trace	6	2
Mayonnaise	110	trace	12	trace
Thousand Island	75	trace	8	1
MISCELLANEOUS ITEMS AND COMBINED INGREDIENTS				
Barbecue sauce, 1/2 cup	91	2	7	8
Beef pot pie	246	10	15	19
Bouillon cube, 1	5	2	trace	trace
Candy, 1 oz.:				
Caramels	120	1	3	22
Chocolate, milk	145	2	9	16
Fudge	115	trace	3	23
Hard candy	110	0	0	28
Marshmallow	95	1	0	23
Chicken á la king	191	11	14	5

Composition of Foods

	Calories	Protein (grams)	Fat (grams)	Carbohydrates (grams)
MISCELLANEOUS ITEMS AND COMBINED INGREDIENTS				
Chicken pot pie	235	10	14	18
Chili con carne, canned beans, 1 serving	133	8	6	12
Chow mein, chicken, no noodles, 1 serving	102	12	4	4
Cole slaw, mayonnaise dressing, 1 serving	144	1	14	5
Fish sticks, frozen, cooked, 1 serving	176	17	9	7
Hollandaise sauce, 1 tbsp.	48	1	4	2
Ice cream, 1 serving	193	5	11	21
Lemonade, 1/2 cup	44	trace	trace	11
Lobster Newburg, 1 serving	194	19	11	5
Lobster salad, 1 serving	110	10	6	2
Macaroni and cheese, 1 serving	215	8	11	20
Nuts:				
Almonds, 1/2 cup	598	19	52	20
Brazil nuts, 1/2 cup	654	14	67	11
Cashew nuts, roasted, 1/2 cup	561	17	6	29
Coconut, dried, shredded, Sweetened, 1 oz.	156	1	11	15
Peanuts:				
Roasted, salted, 1/2 cup	585	26	50	19
Peanut butter, 1 tbsp.	93	4	8	3
Pecans, chopped, 1 tbsp.	50	1	5	1
Walnuts, 1 tbsp.	50	1	5	1
Pheasant, roasted, 1 serving	151	24	5	0
Pizza, 1 serving:				
Cheese topping	236	12	8	28
Sausage topping	234	8	9	30
Potato salad, 1 serving	145	3	9	13
Rabbit, stewed, 1 serving	216	30	10	0
Spaghetti, meatballs, tomato sauce, 1 serving	134	8	5	16
Sugar, 1 oz.	110	0	0	28
Tuna salad, 1 serving	170	15	11	4
Turkey pot pie	237	10	14	19
Waffles, mix, 2 medium size	356	9	2	76

CHAPTER THIRTEEN
SPECIAL PEOPLE/SPECIAL INFORMATION

Shift Workers (Doctors, Nurses, Police, Fire Personnel, Factory Workers)

A "shift worker," no matter what the shift, has a distinct advantage over other travelers when he or she opts to travel in an easterly or westerly direction. If you are already working the night shift, from midnight to 8 AM for example, you are seven or eight hours "phase-advanced" from other travelers headed in the same direction. More than other travelers, you can step right into a new local time frame with little, if any, disruption of your body clocks or circadian rhythms.

The perfect example would be a trip from the United States to Europe. If you are a night shift worker, your day begins about six or eight hours earlier than everyone else's in your community, and since a trip to London entails a time zone change of plus-six hours, you should be able to adjust to daytime life in England very, very easily.

If you are working the afternoon shift, from 4 PM to midnight, select a destination where your hometown nighttime is daytime someplace else, or about minus-eight time zones away in a westerly direction. Since you are already accustomed to being active at night, if you travel to a destination on nearly the other side of the world (the United States to Japan or Honolulu, for example, you should not experience any jet lag at all. All you really have to do is figure out where in the world the local daytime activities correspond to your normal active phase. It is easy.

Gamblers

Much of the gambling that takes place in casinos around the world begins in the evening hours and extends into the wee hours of the next day. Although many casinos are actually open twenty-four hours a day, the majority of the activity and the bigger crowds tend to descend upon the casino at night.

Whether you are an inveterate gambler or just an occasional dabbler, you would do well to consider your body clocks, along with your wallet or pocketbook, when you decide to take a seat at a gaming table. As a daytime creature disposed to perform best during daytime hours, if you are going to a casino where you will have to "turn night into day" by being up most of the night at your destination, pick a location where your body clocks can actually give you an advantage over other players. For example, if you are from New York, Philadelphia, or Miami, if you travel to Monaco or Evian (time change plus six hours), when it is midnight at your destination, it is only 6 PM according to your body clocks. While everyone else at the tables is experiencing the onslaught of disrupted body clocks, you will still be wide-eyed and alert. If you are a West Coast resident and travel to Atlantic City in New Jersey, when it is 2 AM on the East Coast, and everyone is fading, it is only 11 PM, according to your body clocks.

In fact, it is far preferable to leave your hometown to gamble, even if your hometown is Las Vegas—where gambling takes place predominantly at night—and travel to another town where, again, you can have the advantages of the "active" phase of your daily rhythms during everyone else's "inactive" phase. Of course, the key would be to remain on hometown time throughout your gambling trip.

Athletes

The Cure for Jet Lag significantly shortens the duration of jet lag symptoms on a short haul, easterly/westerly flight of under six hours. However, as dramatically effective as the 3-Step System is, and even though it can greatly reduce the weeks it can often take to completely readjust to a new time frame, the 3-Step System does take a few days to do its job on extremely long flights involving multiple time zone changes.

That is why, if you are an athlete, or a concert performer, or even a diplomat who simply must be at his best at a specific time of day, you should plan to arrive at your destination early. How early? It depends upon how many time zones you have flown through, and whether you have traveled in an easterly or westerly direction, gaining or losing time.

The human body performs in cycles, performing certain tasks better at one time of the day than it does at another time of the day. For example, if you are going to perform a more mental task, such as balancing the checkbook, chronobiologists know that the best time to attempt it is between 2 PM and 3 PM. This is the proved period of increased mental acuity within the human's circadian or daily body rhythm. Therefore, if you are an athlete, in order to do your best, you have to know at what time of day you are going to be at peak physical prowess. The answer is throughout the active phase of the day, until about 4 PM or 6 PM. At any other time of day, you are working against your natural body rhythms, and you will not derive maximum benefits from exercise or practice.

When you are at home base, of course, you can tell what the best time is to perform or practice just by looking at the clock. If possible, you can schedule events with knowledge of circadian rhythms in mind, and know that you, indeed, are giving it your best shot. However, when you intend to compete after a rapid flight that involves a time frame change, you must allow your body rhythms to resynchronize to local time. If you do not, you will be competing with a body that simply cannot function optimally, and against competitors who are at a distinct physical advantage.

The Cure for Jet Lag can and does force a rapid resynchronization, but realistically, the system cannot work an "overnight" miracle when severe time frame changes are involved. You must check the Best Day of Arrival chart in Chapter Six and allow yourself (if it is at all possible) those few days required for the rapid resynchronization process to work. Arrive early enough at your destination to really get your body clocks well into synchronization before the event.

Also, a note about *burnout*. Sometimes athletes just seem to lose the ability to compete. When this is the case, poor sleep may be the culprit. Sleep loss can totally disrupt your timing, coordination, personality, and sense of well-being. The remedy for burnout may well be to go to bed, not back to the gym, when your athletic prowess seems to be waning. Regular sleep patterns are vital for maximum performance. Follow *The Cure for Jet Lag's* high-protein breakfast and lunch, and high-carbohydrate supper plan. Almost overnight you should be able to stabilize your sleep/wake patterns.

Anyone Taking Drugs

Throughout the course of a twenty-four-hour day, levels of insulin, blood pressure, cholesterol, red blood cells, white blood cells, and other physiological properties and processes fluctuate. When a prescription label reads "take one in the morning" or "take one four times per day," the dosage is predicated on a scientific understanding of the human body's chemistry, and how it will react to the drug during a particular phase of your twenty-four-hour cycle.

New sleep/wake patterns, new meal times, and other conditions associated with time zone changes result in discordance of your entire body chemistry. As your body chemistry changes, you become *more* or *less* sensitive to drugs, depending upon the state of your body chemistry. Occasionally, what was a beneficial dosage may even prove debilitating or fatal. *You must speak to your doctor about drug effects prior to flight.* If you are diabetic, hypertensive, or asthmatic, or if you are taking any drugs whatsoever for any reason, your medication dosage and timing must be adjusted to compensate for periods when internal body clocks are phasing forward or backward to synchronize to the new time frame.

Women

The menstrual cycle of women appears to be controlled by a number of environmental factors, including the light/dark patterns of the twenty-four-hour day. Many women who have irregular (or nonexistent) menstrual cycles are thought by chronobiologists to be out of synchronization with their environment. For example, flight attendants, doctors, nurses, fire and police personnel, and waiters, who work odd hours and in "shifts," often have to turn "night into day" and "day into night" in order to perform their jobs. Because humans are daytime creatures, working a night shift wreaks havoc with natural body rhythms, as does working a split-shift, or circumnavigating the globe.

For women with menstrual problems, *The Cure for Jet Lag* may prove a boon because it literally forces the reestablishment of a defined daily body rhythm. The other side of the coin, however, is that a long-distance, rapid flight to a new time zone will disrupt a stabilized menstrual rhythm. But, in both cases, *The Cure for Jet Lag* can remedy the situation.

The Elderly

As human beings get older, many circadian or daily rhythms alter or slow down measurably. Sleep, for example, tends to become fragmented, and the metabolic rate can decrease by as much as 30%. Although scientists are not exactly sure what the cause or causes may be, the theory is that the overall degenerative process inherent in aging also takes its toll on body rhythms, causing them to operate less efficiently and in poorer synchronization as the years go by. For this reason, shifting body clocks to a new time frame after a lengthy east or west flight may prove to be a very difficult ordeal for the elderly, particularly without *The Cure for Jet Lag*.

However, *The Cure for Jet Lag* has the potential to help the elderly resynchronize their body clocks. For the first time in many years, perhaps many decades, the elderly should be able to assume a better-defined pattern of daily rhythms that result in a real feeling of improved well-being. All the ailments associated with disrupted daily body clocks (irritability, fatigue, constipation, headache, insomnia, inability to concentrate, etc.) should improve markedly once body rhythms fall back into proper synchronization. *The Cure for Jet Lag* could prove extraordinarily helpful to the elderly.

Pilots and Air Crew Members

Some pilots and air crew members take to their beds immediately upon landing at their destination. They pull down the shades, turn off the lights, possibly take a drink or a sleeping pill—and hope for the best in sleep. Others never take a nap, but plunge right into destination time activities, and as the day proceeds, they proceed to enter a stage of exhaustion and circadian chaos. In other words, each crew member has his own remedy and methodology for dealing with jet lag. Some crew members give in to jet lag, and others fight it. But who fares best? The answer is neither.

Nor is the situation likely to change soon, at least not with the current flight options and rest periods that are available to flight personnel. The pilot or air crew member who has flown through the night is physically exhausted from being up all day and all night, and is now combining natural exhaustion with body rhythm dyschronism. When he gets to his hotel, the best he can hope for is a nap. There is no way his sleep will be anything but fragmented and inadequate. By taking a drink or a sleeping pill, in actuality, he exacerbates the problem. Drugs (and sleeping pills and alcohol are drugs) may make your eyes close and may make you lose consciousness, but the sleep they promote is woefully inadequate. In fact, drugs cause the body, whether in a state of consciousness or unconsciousness, to work hard to rid itself of alien chemicals during the time it should be totally involved in the recuperative sleep process. So you wake up as tired, or more tired, than before. Also, recent research has shown that there is a hangover effect associated with commonly used sleep-inducers that lasts much longer than originally thought. Twenty-four hours after taking an over-the-counter sleep remedy, the effects can still be felt. *The Cure for Jet Lag* will be useful only when there is time for implementation: during a leave of absence, while on a vacation, or if a large block of time exists between flights.

However, there are a number of relaxation techniques available which, in fact, do help promote relaxation and sleep. Of course, putting these techniques into effect requires some education, motivation, and self-discipline. The following is a list of techniques that pilots, crews, and cabin attendants have reported as useful.

Relaxation Response. Likened by some authorities to the techniques of transcendental meditation, the relaxation response was described by Herbert Benson, M.D., of the Harvard Medical School. Dr. Benson has you sit upright in a comfortable position (although some people prefer to lie down) close your eyes, and repeat the word "one" over and over again. Through this constant repetition, you eliminate extraneous thought from your consciousness and begin to feel a sense of calm and well-being which often progresses to sleep. When you awake or arise, you feel refreshed. Since the relaxation response technique does not involve a change in lifestyle or philosophy, it should be easy to implement.

Autogenic Training Technique. Developed by J. Schultz and refined over the years by W. Luthe, the Autogenic Training Technique involves repeating suggestions of warmth and heaviness over and over again. This technique has been used in studies of insomniacs and does, indeed, prove to be very effective in reducing the amount of time it takes to fall asleep. It also seems to enhance the quality of that sleep. As a byproduct, it has been found that physiological and emotional tolerances are increased as well.

Hatha Yoga. Hatha yoga is considered the most basic type of yoga you can master. Concerned mainly with physical postures ("asanas"), hatha yoga involves assuming a variety of positions, either standing, sitting, or lying down (on your back or front), which enable you to relax through breathing exercises, and ultimately, to sleep. Not to be confused with other branches of yoga, for example Kundalini or Raja yoga, which involve the spiritual more than the physical, hatha yoga works well as a relaxation technique with full benefits realized after postures are perfected.

Midnight Fliers

Red-eye flights—and all other variations that require staying up very late to catch a flight—disrupt sleep patterns as significantly as the changing of time zones. It may be economical, but the midnight flight wreaks havoc with your body's natural rhythms and body clocks.

In order to counter the problems of the late-night departures, you should implement *The Cure for Jet Lag* as you would for any daytime or early evening flight from coast to coast. When traveling in an easterly direction (California to New York), when the 3-Step System calls for "methylated xanthines," take them as scheduled, stay awake until you get on the airplane, and then rest or sleep as soundly as possible. The fact that your plane does not take off until very late at night, or the wee hours of the morning, should not interfere with the actual timing of the 3-Step System. When traveling in a westerly direction (New York to California), on the morning of the flight drink the "methylated xanthines" as prescribed, and continue the System accordingly, slipping onto California time with breakfast on destination time, and remaining alert until sleep time on the West Coast.

Travelers By Sea

If you have the time and the inclination, cruising may well be the most advantageous way to avoid jet lag on easterly and westerly journeys. When you cruise, if you leave by ship from your *own* time zone, you do not get severe jet lag symptoms. Ships move too slowly. By the time your ship drops anchor at its final destination, you will have naturally, over the course of your days at sea, become synchronized with the local time frame, and you will not need any 3-Step System at all. However, if your cruise begins after a long trans-meridional flight (Europe, Asia, Australia to the Caribbean, for example), make sure you implement the 3-Step System that is appropriate for your point of departure by *ship*. If you are cruising and then flying, begin the Preflight Steps, in sufficient time, while on board the ship.

APPENDIX

LIST OF CAFFEINATED BEVERAGES AND FOODS

Know your caffeine sources so you can avoid accidentally drinking beverages, eating food, chewing gum or taking pills that contain caffeine. When *The Cure for Jet Lag* calls for avoiding them, refer to the list that follows. Its sources include the online website caffeinefiend.com, The Center for Science in the Public Interest (a health advocacy group), The USDA Agricultural Research Service, *Food & Chemical Toxicology,* and *The Journal of Analytical Toxicology.*

CAFFEINE FOUND IN DRINKS		
Note that caffeine amounts are for whole can/bottle		
NAME	**Ounces**	**Caffeine (mg)**
180	8.2	90
7-Up	12	0
A&W Cream Soda	12	29
Afri Cola	12	89
Airforce Nutrisoda Energize	8.45	50
Ale 8.1	12	37
Ammo	1	171
Amp	8.4	75
Amp Overdrive	16	142
Arizona Extreme Energy Shot	8.3	100
Arizona Green Tea Energy	16	200
Barq's Red Crème Soda	12	0
Barq's Root Beer	12	22.5
Battery	11.2	106
Bawls	10	66.7
Bazza High Energy Tea	16.9	150
Beaver Buzz	8.3	110
Big Red	12	34
Blow (Energy Drink Mix)	8	240
Bomba Energy	8.4	75

List of Caffeinated Beverages and Foods

CAFFEINE FOUND IN DRINKS		
Note that caffeine amounts are for whole can/bottle		
NAME	**Ounces**	**Caffeine (mg)**
Boo-Koo Energy	24	360
Brawndo	16	200
Burn	8.3	118
Burn (UK)	8.45	45
Burn2	16	199
BuzzWater	16.9	200
Celsius	12	200
Cheerwine	12	47.5
Cherry Coke	12	34
Chic	12	150
Chocolate Milk	8	5
Clearly Canadian Daily Energy	20	80
Club-Mate	16.9	100
Coca-Cola Blak	8	46
Coca-Cola	12	34
Coca-Cola Classic	12	34.5
Coca-Cola Zero	12	34.5
Cocaine Energy Drink	8.4	280
Coffee (Brewed)	8	107.5
Coffee (Decaf, Brewed)	8	5.6
Coffee (Decaf, Instant)	8	2.5
Coffee (Drip)	8	145
Coffee (Expresso)	1.5	77
Coffee (Instant)	8	57
Crunk	8.3	100
Crystal Light Energy	16	120
Crystal Light Iced Tea	8	11.25
Daredevil	16	240
Diablo	8.4	95
Diet A&W Cream Soda	12	22
Diet Cheerwine	12	48.1

CAFFEINE FOUND IN DRINKS		
Note that caffeine amounts are for whole can/bottle		
NAME	**Ounces**	**Caffeine (mg)**
Diet Cherry Coca-Cola	12	34
Diet Coke	12	45
Diet Coke with Lemon	12	45
Diet Coke with Lime	12	45
Diet Coke with Splenda	12	34
Diet Dr. Pepper	12	41
Diet Mello Yello	12	51
Diet Mountain Dew	12	55
Diet Dr. Pibb	12	40
Diet Pepsi	12	36
Diet Pepsi Max	12	69
Diet RC Cola	12	47.3
Diet Ruby Red Squirt	12	39
Diet Sunkist Orange Soda	12	42
Diet Vanilla Coke	12	45
Diet Wild Cherry Pepsi	12	36
Dopamine Energy Drink	8.4	120
Dr Pepper	12	41
Enviga	12	100
Faygo Cola	12	41.7
Faygo Moon Mist	12	19.7
Fixx	20	500
Fritz Kola	11.16	83.3
FRS Antioxidant Health Drink	11	38
Fuel Cell	2	180
Full Throttle	16	144
Game Juice	16.9	38
Go Fast	11.9	120
Guru	8.3	125
H2O Blast	16	100
Hansen's Energy Pro	8.3	57

List of Caffeinated Beverages and Foods

CAFFEINE FOUND IN DRINKS		
Note that caffeine amounts are for whole can/bottle		
NAME	**Ounces**	**Caffeine (mg)**
Havoc	8.4	52
Hiball Energy	10	75
Hogan Energy	16	160
Hot Cocoa	8	5
Howling Monkey	16	160
Hydrive	11	121
Hype	8.4	80
Inko's White Tea Energy	15.5	184
Jave Chai	8	120
Joker	16	150
Jolt Cola	23.5	220
Jolt Endurance Shot	2	150
Jones Energy	16	100
Kaboom Infinite Energy	8	95
Lipton Brisk (all varieties)	12	9
Lipton Iced Tea	20	50
Lucozade	12.85	46
Ludicrous	16	0
McDonald's Large Coffee	16	145
McDonald's Small Coffee	12	109
MDX	14	82.25
MDX, Sugar Free	14	87.5
Mello Yello	12	52.5
Monster	16	160
Morning Spark	16.9	170
Mother	11.18	106
Mountain Dew	12	55
Mountain Dew Baja Blast	8	36
Mountain Dew Code Red	12	54
Mountain Dew Game Fuel	20	120
Naked Juice Energy Smoothie	15.2	81.7

CAFFEINE FOUND IN DRINKS		
Note that caffeine amounts are for whole can/bottle		
NAME	**Ounces**	**Caffeine (mg)**
Nestea Iced Tea	16	34
Nestea Peach Green Tea	20	42.4
Nestea Sweetened Lemon Tea	20	27.5
No Name Energy Drink	8.4	280
NOS	16	250
Nuclear Waste Antidote	16	180
O Infused Water- Energize	16	64
Ol' Glory	16	100
Oregon Chai (Concentrate)	4	32.5
Pacific Chai	12	100
Pepsi One	12	55
Pepsi-Cola	12	38
Pibb Xtra	12	40.5
Pibb Zero	12	40.5
Pimp Juice	8.3	81
Power Edge	8	80
Power Horse	8.45	80
Powershot	1	100
Propel Invigorating Water	20	50
Rage	16	200
RC Cola	12	45.2
RC Cola, Cherry	12	43.2
Red Bull	8.3	80
Red Devil	8.4	41.8
Red Flash	12	37
Red Jak	16	164
Red Rock Cola	12	26.1
Redline RTD	8	250
Relentless	16.9	180
Rip It Energy Fuel	8	100
Ritz Cola	12	10.3

List of Caffeinated Beverages and Foods

CAFFEINE FOUND IN DRINKS		
Note that caffeine amounts are for whole can/bottle		
NAME	Ounces	Caffeine (mg)
Rockstar	16	160
Rockstar Energy Cola	16	150
Rockstar Juiced	16	160
Rockstar Roasted	15	225
Rockstar Zero Carb	16	240
Ruby Red Squirt	12	39
Rumba Energy Juice	16	170
Rush! Energy	8.3	50
Shark	8.4	80
Shasta Cola	12	42.9
Silk Soylatte	8	55
Sky Rocket Caffeinated Syrup	1	100
Slim-Fast Cappuccino Shake	12	40
Snapple Elements	18	108
Snapple Tea	12	31.5
SoBe Adrenaline Rush	8.3	79
SoBe Energy Citrus	20	80
SoBe Essential Energy	16	96
SoBe Green Tea	20	35
SoBe No Fear	16	174
SoBe No Fear Gold	16	174
Socko	16	160
Socko Slim	16	160
Spark	8	120
SPIKE Shooter	8.4	300
Sprite	12	0
Starbucks Bottled Frappucino	9.5	90
Starbucks Double Shot	6.5	130
Starbucks Grande Caffe Amer	16	225
Starbucks Grande Caffe Latte	16	150
Starbucks Grande Caffe Mocha	16	175

CAFFEINE FOUND IN DRINKS		
Note that caffeine amounts are for whole can/bottle		
NAME	**Ounces**	**Caffeine (mg)**
Starbucks Grande Cappuccino	16	150
Starbucks Grande Coffee	16	330
Starbucks Grande Decaf Coffee	16	12.7
Starbucks Short Coffee	8	180
Starbucks Tall Caffe Amer	12	150
Starbucks Tall Caffe Latte	12	75
Starbucks Tall Caffe Mocha	12	95
Starbucks Tall Cappuccino	12	75
Starbucks Tall Coffee	12	260
Starbucks Tall Decaf Coffee	12	9.5
Stok Black Coffee Shots	0.44	40
Sun Drop	12	63
Sunkist Orange Soda	12	41
Superfly	8	150
TaB	12	46.5
TaB Energy	10.5	95
Tazo Chai	8	47
Tea (Brewed)	8	47
Tea (Brewed, Imported)	8	60
Tea (Green)	8	25
Tea (Iced)	8	47
Tea (Instant)	8	26
Tonic Water	11.9	0
Trim Water	20	50
Tropicana Twister Soda	20	0
Upshot	2.5	2.00
V	11.85	109
Vamp	16	240
Vanilla Coke	12	34
Vault	12	70
Viso Energy Vigor	20	300

List of Caffeinated Beverages and Foods

CAFFEINE FOUND IN DRINKS		
Note that caffeine amounts are for whole can/bottle		
NAME	**Ounces**	**Caffeine (mg)**
Vital Lifestye Water – Energize	20	60
Vitamin Energy	16	150
Vitamin Water Energy Citrus	20	42
Von Dutch	16	160
Water Joe	16.9	60
Whey Up	16	150
Who's Your Daddy	16	200
Whoop Ass	8.45	50
Wild Cherry Pepsi	12	38
Wilfred X344	16	344
XS	8.4	83
WTZ Tea	12	154
ZipFizz Energy Drink Mix	16	100

CAFFEINE FOUND IN MINTS, CHOCOLATE AND GUM			
NAME	**Type**	**Caffeine (mg)**	**Per**
Bawls Mints	Mints	5	mint
Black Black Gum	Gum	5	piece
Buzz Bites Chocolate Chews	Choc	100	chew
Clif Shot Bloks	Candy	16.17	piece
Dannon Coffee Yogurt	Yogurt	36	tub, 6 oz
Diablo Energy Strip	Strips	25	strip
Foosh Energy Mints	Mints	100	mint
Haagen-Dazs Coffee Ice Cream	Ice Cream	48	cup, 8 oz
Headshot	Bars	22	bar
Hershey's Chocolate Bar	Choc	9	bar
Hershey's Kisses	Choc	1	kiss
Hershey's Special Dark	Choc	18	bar
Hershey's with Almonds	Choc	8	bar
Jolt Gum	Gum	12.7	piece

CAFFEINE FOUND IN MINTS, CHOCOLATE AND GUM			
NAME	Type	Caffeine (mg)	Per
Kickbutt Amped Energy Ballz	Balls	40	ball
Kit Kat	Candy	6	bar
M-60 Energy Mints	Mints	7	mint
Mad-Croc Energy Chews	Chews	8	piece
Mad-Croc Energy Gum	Gum	40	piece
NRage Energy Strips	Strips	20	strip
Oral Fixation Night Light Mints	Mints	1.9	mint
Penguin Chocolate Mints	Mints	7	mint
Penguin Mints	Mints	7	mint
Penguin Reds	Mints	7	mint
Peppgum	Gum	77	piece
Reese's Peanut Butter Cups	Candy	4	cup
Rocket Chocolate	Choc	42	piece
Vojo Energy Mints	Mints	2.2	mint
Wharp Energy Green Tea	Mints	10	mint
Warp Energy Mints	Mints	10	mint
XTZ Energy Mints	Mints	15	mint
Zingos Mints	Mints	15	mint

Itinerary Worksheet

Flights	Flying Time	Time Change	Nights at Destination

Itinerary Worksheet

Flights	Flying Time	Time Change	Nights at Destination

Itinerary Worksheet

Flights	Flying Time	Time Change	Nights at Destination

Itinerary Worksheet

Flights	Flying Time	Time Change	Nights at Destination

Itinerary Worksheet

Flights	Flying Time	Time Change	Nights at Destination

ABOUT THE AUTHORS

Lynne Waller Scanlon

Lynne Waller Scanlon is publisher of Back2Press Books, and the coauthor with the late Charles F. Ehret, Ph.D, of *Overcoming Jet Lag*, now updated and re-titled *The Cure for Jet Lag*. She also has written or coauthored two previous international bestsellers with hundreds of thousands of copies in print: *The 21st Century Diet* published by St. Martin's Press and *5-Day Allergy Relief System* published by HarperCollins Publishers. She has appeared on radio and TV throughout the country. Her international literary blog, www.thepublishingcontrarian.com, receives hundreds of thousands of page hits each year.

Charles F. Ehret, Ph.D.
(March 3, 1923 – February 24, 2007)

Charles F. Ehret was a pioneer in Chronobiology and Chronotechnology, the discoverer and developer of the first multifaceted (multi-*zeitgeber*) system to minimize the effects of jet lag and of shift work fatigue. He was the coauthor with Lynne Waller Scanlon of the international best-seller, *Overcoming Jet Lag*, originally published by Berkley Publishing. He also was the author of *Chronobiotechnology & Chronobiological Engineering* (NATO Science Series E) published by Springer Publishing Company.